MANSUN ·ATTACK OF THE GR

PolyGram Music Publishing Limited

Exclusive Distributors:
Music Sales Limited
8/9 Frith Street, London W1V 5TZ, England.
Music Sales Pty Limited
120 Rothschild Avenue, Rosebery,
NSW 2018, Australia.

Order No.AM943822
ISBN 0-7119-6538-2

Visit the Internet Music Shop at
http://www.musicsales.co.uk

Music arranged by Arthur Dick.
Music processed by Seton Music Graphics.
Front cover photograph courtesy Merton Gauster.

Printed in the United Kingdom by
Halstan & Co Limited, Amersham, Buckinghamshire.

Your Guarantee of Quality:
As publishers, we strive to produce every
book to the highest commercial standards.
The music has been freshly engraved and,
whilst endeavouring to retain the original running
order of the recorded album, the book has been
carefully designed to minimise awkward page
turns and to make playing from it a real pleasure.
Particular care has been given to specifying
acid-free, neutral-sized paper made from pulps
which have not been elemental chlorine bleached.
This pulp is from farmed sustainable forests and
was produced with special regard for the environment.
Throughout, the printing and binding have been
planned to ensure a sturdy, attractive publication
which should give years of enjoyment.
If your copy fails to meet our high standards,
please inform us and we will gladly replace it.

Music Sales' complete catalogue describes
thousands of titles and is available in full colour
sections by subject, direct from Music Sales Limited.
Please state your areas of interest and send a
cheque/postal order for £1.50 for postage to:
Music Sales Limited, Newmarket Road,
Bury St. Edmunds, Suffolk IP33 3YB.

TABLATURE & INSTRUCTIONS EXPLAINED

The tablature stave comprises six lines, each representing a string on the guitar as illustrated.

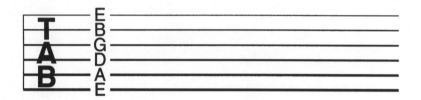

A number on any of the lines indicates, therefore, the string and fret on which a note should be played.

4th String	3rd String	3rd String	3rd String	1st String	OPEN	
7th Fret	7th Fret	5th Fret	OPEN	2nd String	1st Fret	Chord of
5th String				3rd String	2nd Fret	A minor
OPEN				4th String	2nd Fret	
				5th String	OPEN	

A useful hint to help you read tablature is to cut out small squares of self-adhesive paper and stick them on the upper edge of the guitar neck adjacent to each of the frets, numbering them accordingly. Be careful to use paper that will not damage the finish on your guitar.

Finger Vibrato

Tremolo Arm Vibrato

Glissando

Strike the note, then slide the finger up or down the fretboard as indicated.

Tremolo Strumming

This sign indicates fast up and down stroke strumming.

8va

This sign indicates that the notes are to be played an octave higher than written.

loco

This instruction cancels the above.

This note-head indicates the string is to be totally muted to produce a percussive effect.

P.M. = Palm mute

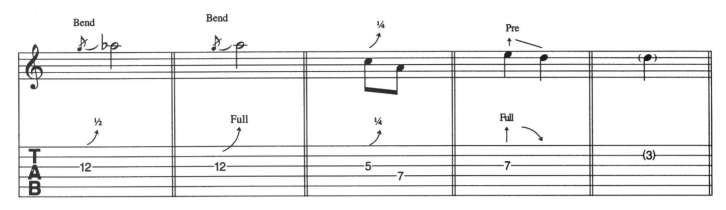

HALF TONE BEND
Play the note G then bend the string so that the pitch rises by a half tone (semi-tone).

FULL TONE BEND

DECORATIVE BEND

PRE-BEND
Bend the string as indicated, strike the string and release.

GHOST NOTE
The note is half sounded

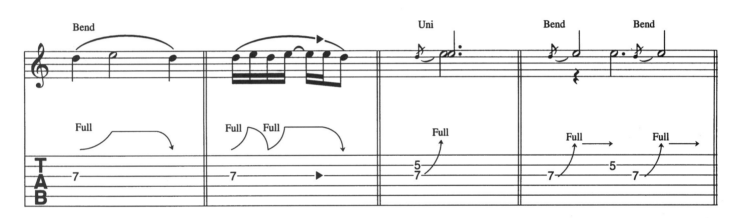

BEND & RELEASE
Strike the string, bend it as indicated, then release the bend whilst it is still sounding.

BEND & RESTRIKE
Strike the string, bend or gliss as indicated, then restrike the string where the symbol occurs.

UNISON BEND
Strike both strings simultaneously then immediately bend the lower string as indicated.

STAGGERED UNISON BEND
Strike the lower string and bend as indicated; whilst it is still sounding strike the higher string.

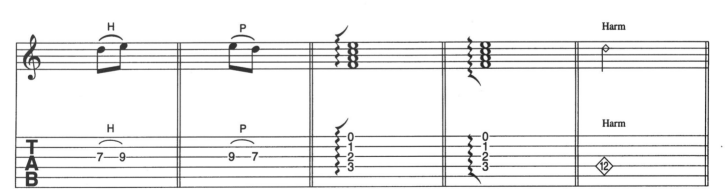

HAMMER-ON
Hammer a finger down on the next note without striking the string again.

PULL-OFF
Pull your finger off the string with a plucking motion to sound the next note without striking the string again.

RAKE-UP
Strum the notes upwards in the manner of an arpeggio.

RAKE-DOWN
Strum the notes downwards in the manner of an arpeggio.

HARMONICS
Strike the string whilst touching it lightly at the fret position shown. Artificial Harmonics, (A.H.), will be described in context.

7

THE CHAD WHO LOVED ME

WORDS & MUSIC BY PAUL DRAPER

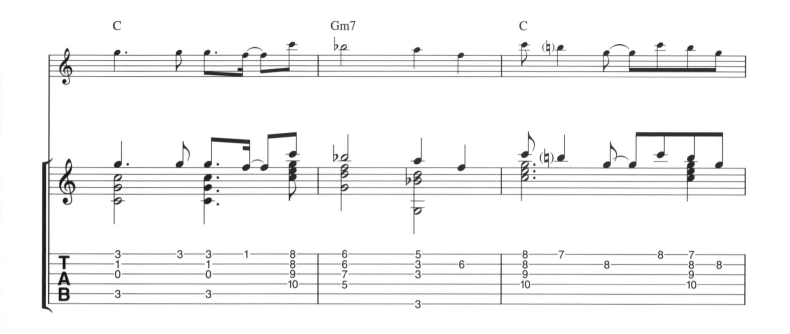

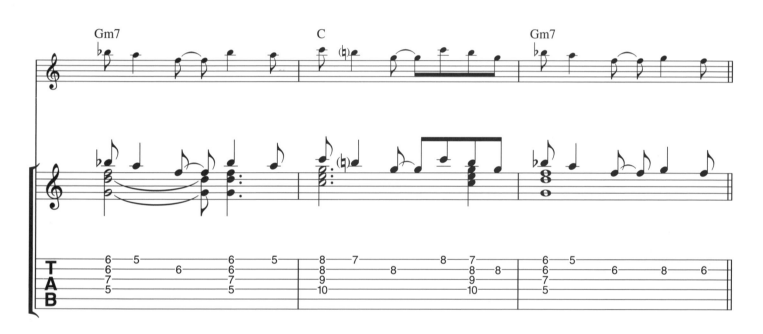

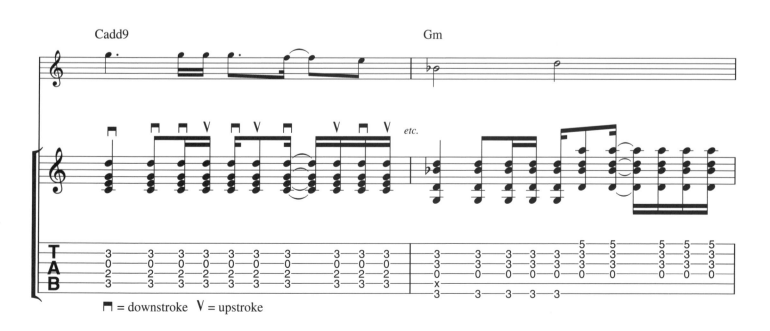

◻ = downstroke V = upstroke

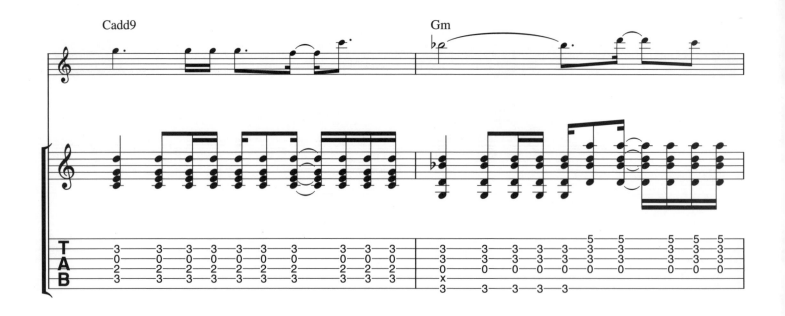

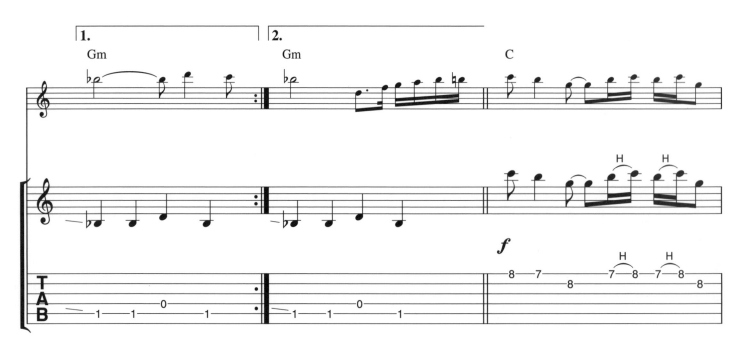

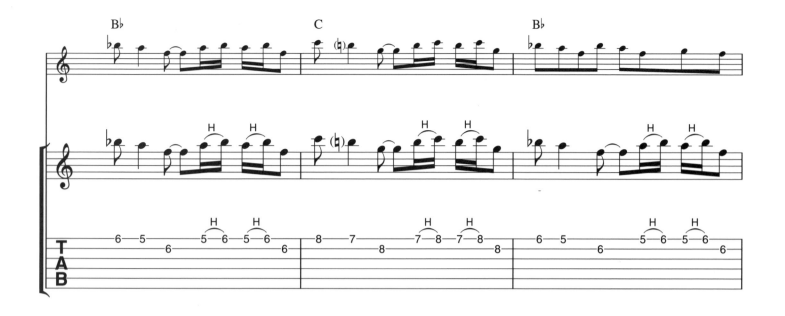

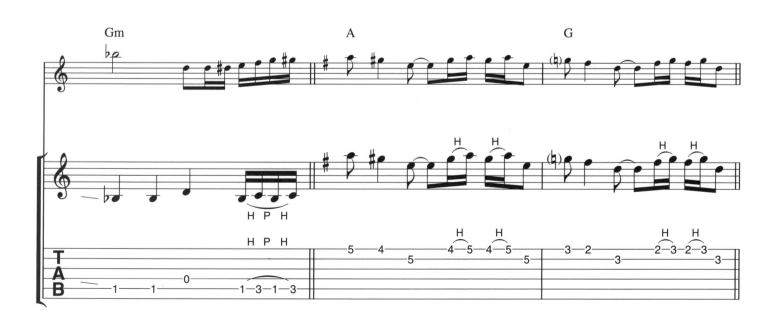

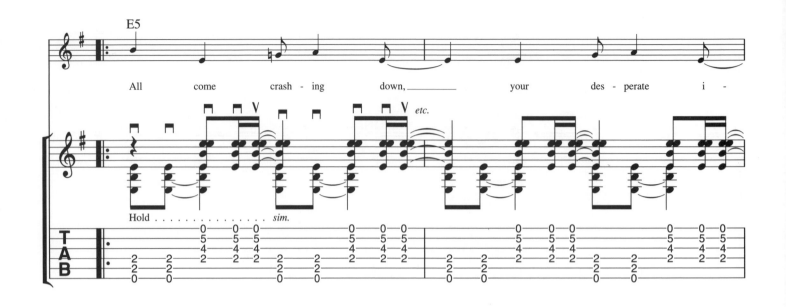

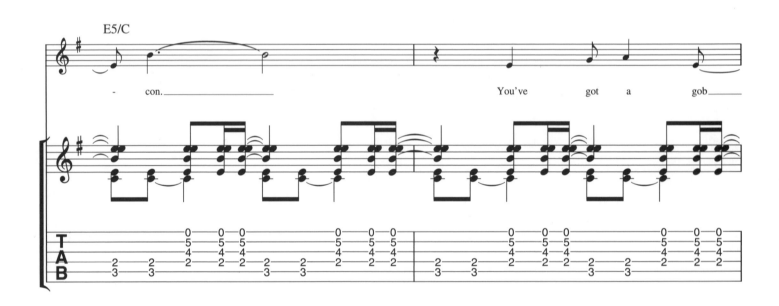

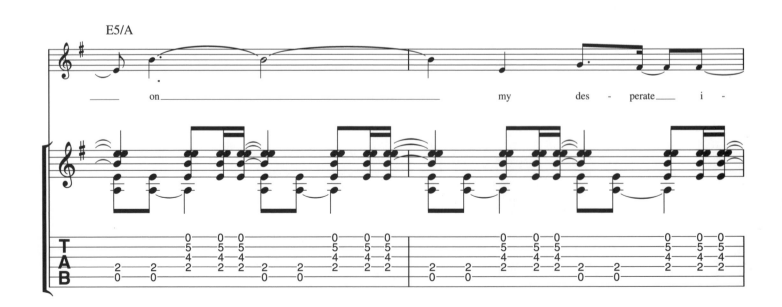

13

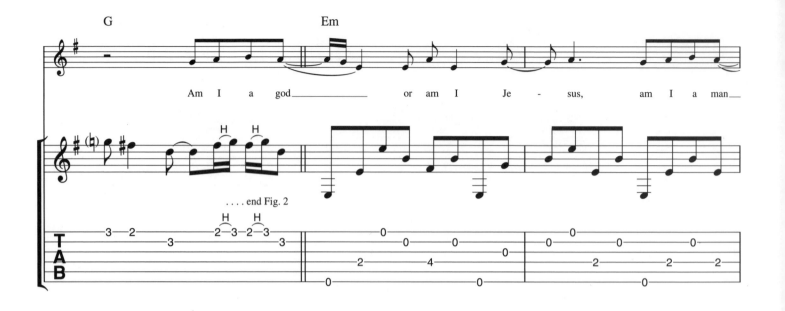

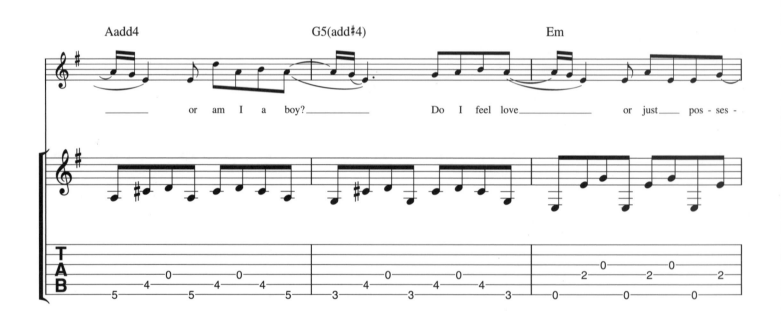

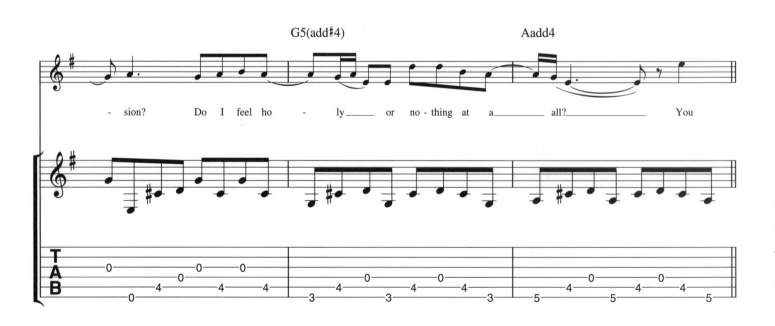

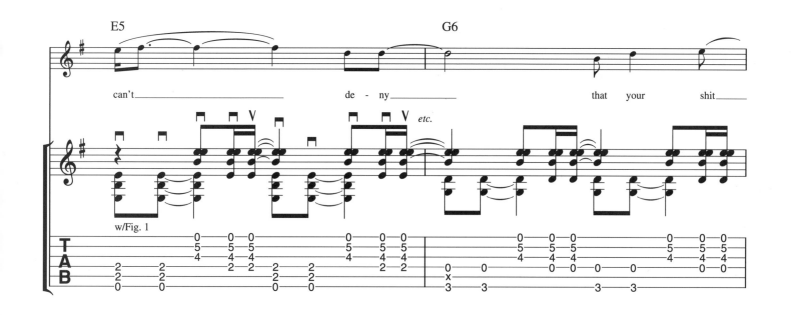

can't_____ de - ny_____ that your shit_____

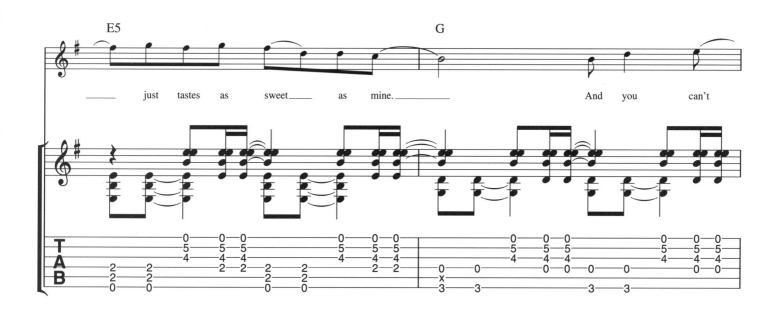

_____ just tastes as sweet_____ as mine._____ And you can't

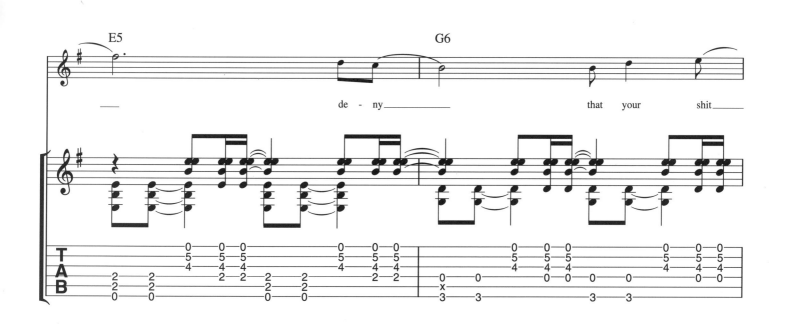

_____ de - ny_____ that your shit_____

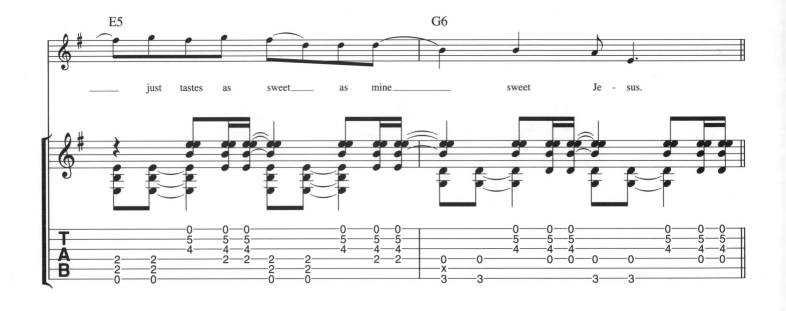

just tastes as sweet___ as mine_____ sweet Je - sus.

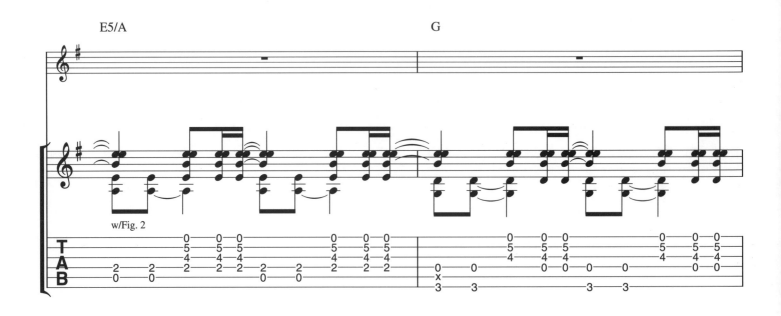

w/Fig. 2

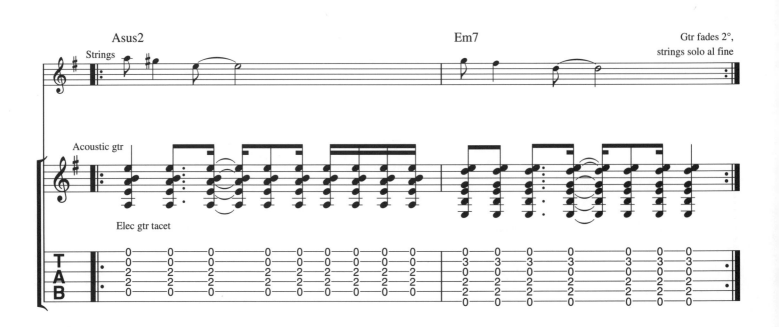

Strings

Acoustic gtr

Elec gtr tacet

Gtr fades 2°,
strings solo al fine

MANSUN'S ONLY LOVE SONG

WORDS & MUSIC BY PAUL DRAPER

* chord & tab in parentheses refer to rhythm voicing

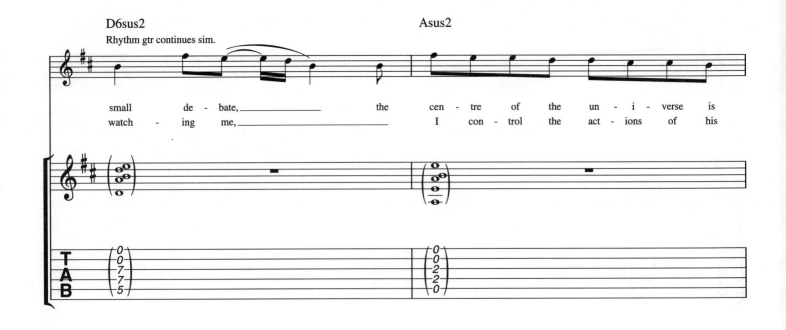

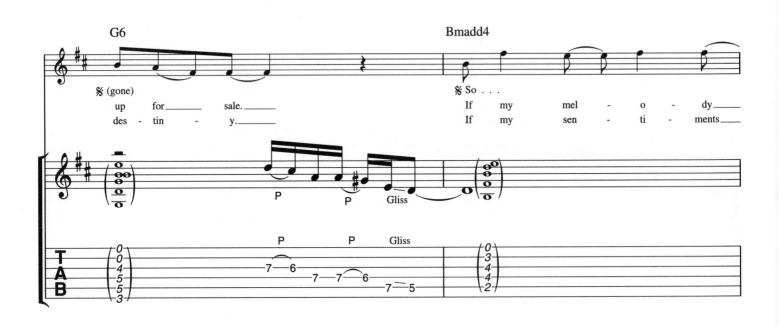

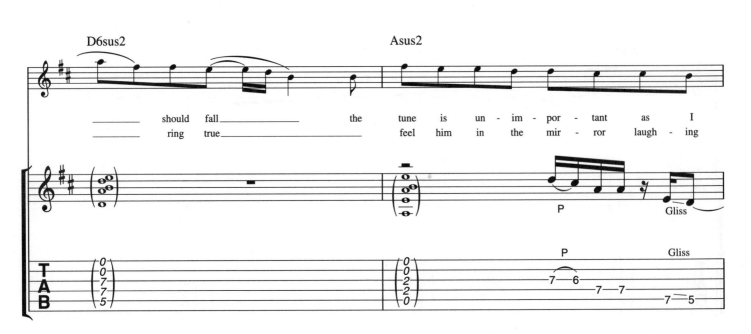

18

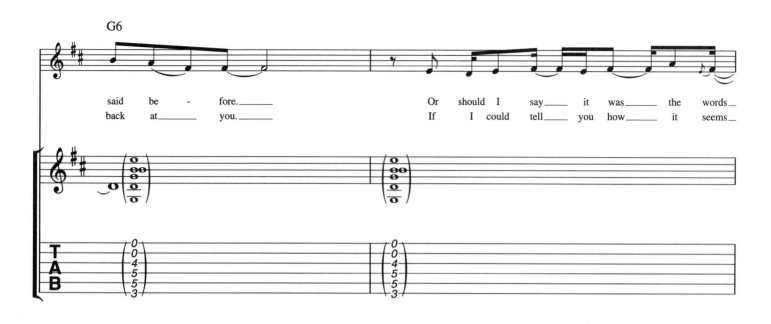

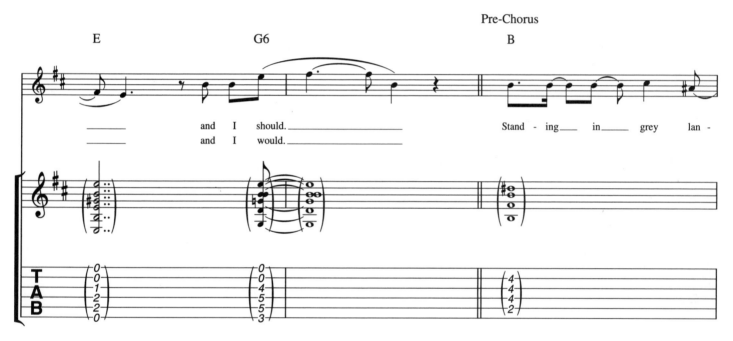

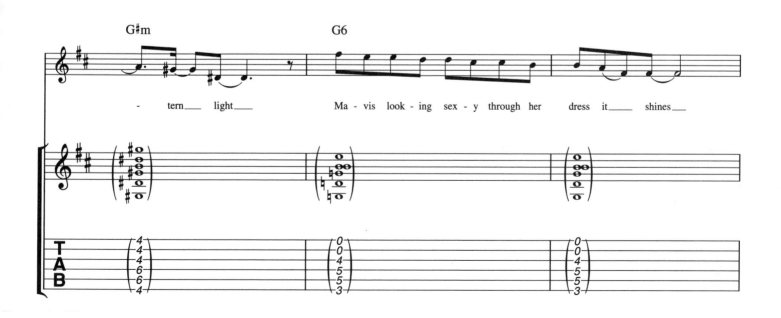

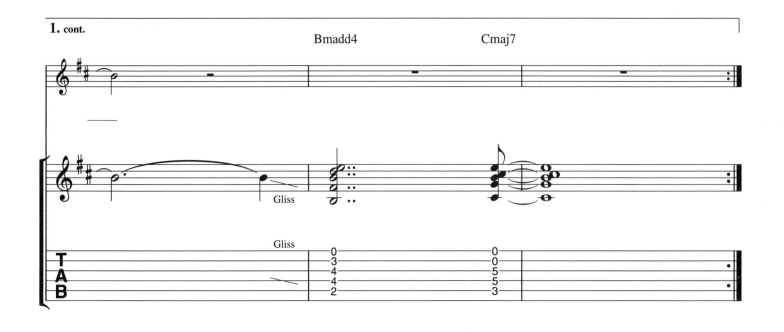

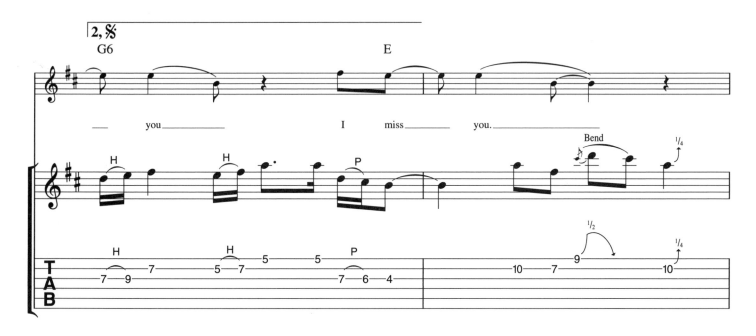

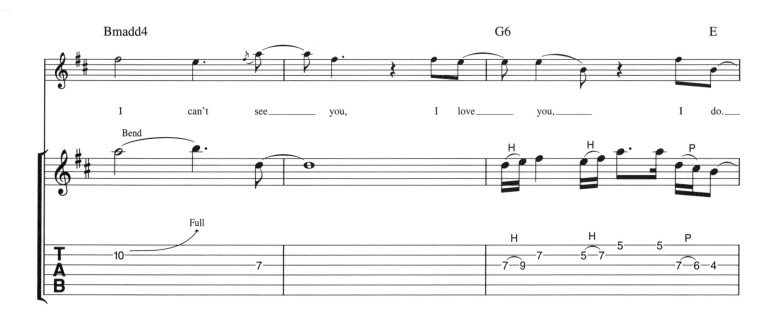

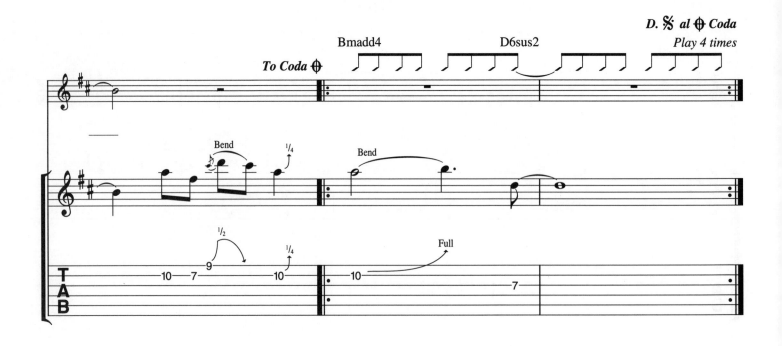

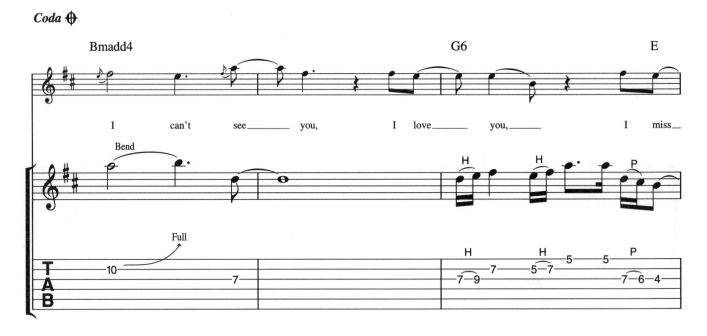

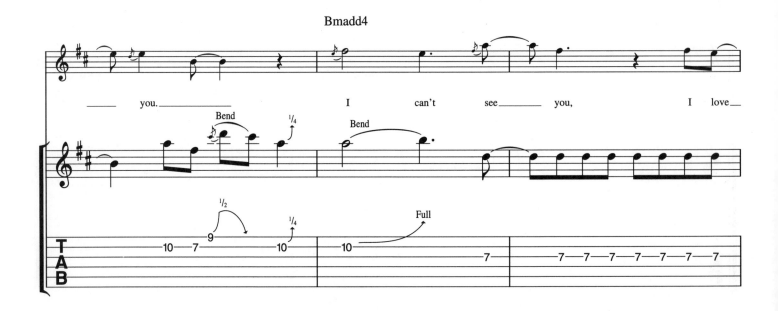

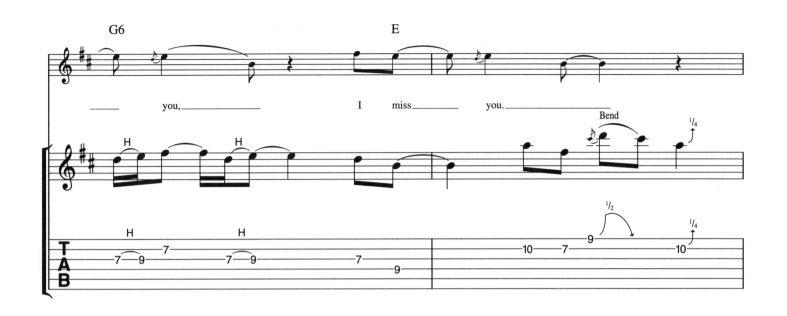

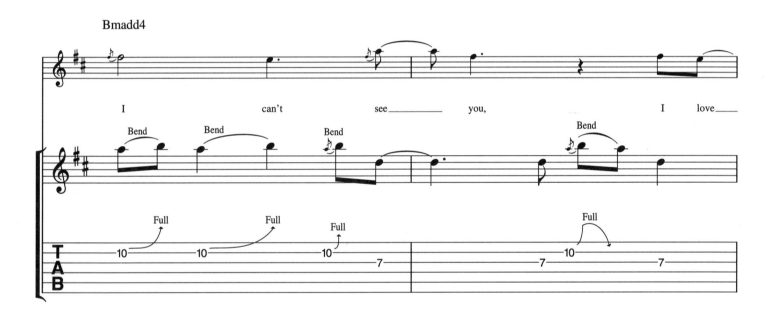

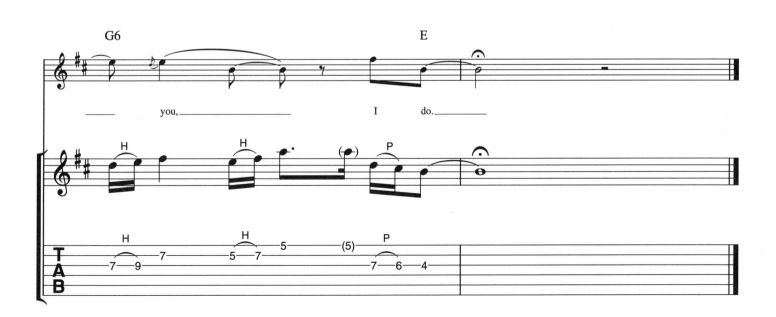

TAXLOSS

WORDS & MUSIC BY PAUL DRAPER

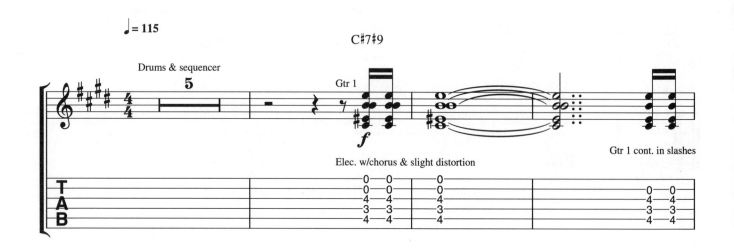

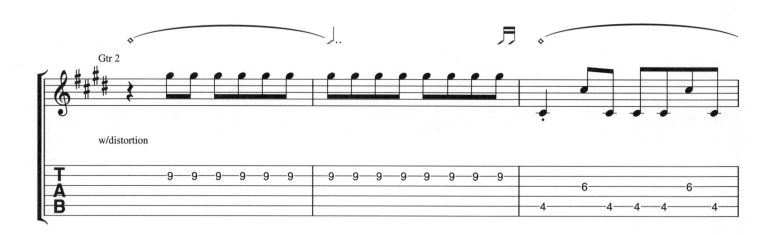

He'll be your

Verse

C#7#9

1. tax - loss lov - er from Liv - er - pool,____ tax - loss lov - er if the
2. & 𝄋 tax - loss lov - er and his name is Bert,____ tax - loss lov - er and he's

Gtr 1

Let ring . . . . sim.
Gtr 2 tacet

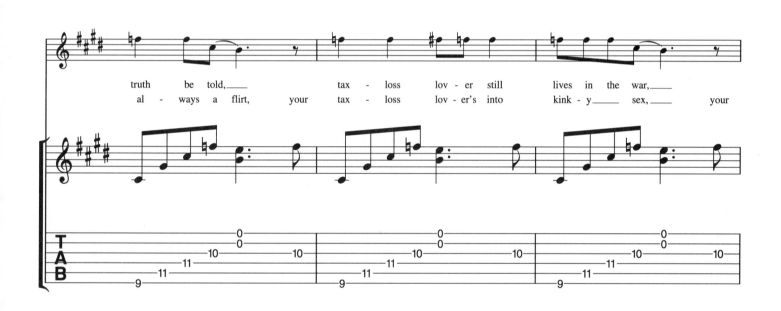

truth be told,____ tax - loss lov - er still lives in the war,____
al - ways a flirt, your tax - loss lov - er's into kink - y____ sex,____ your

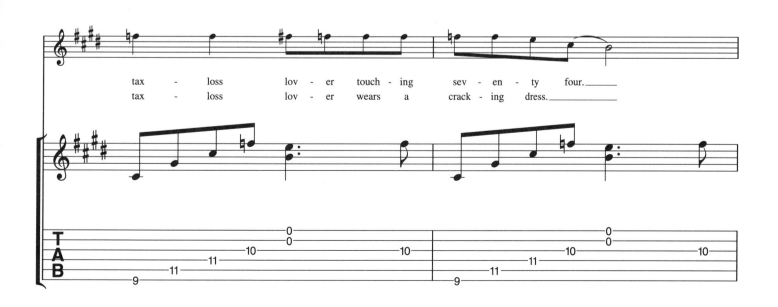

tax - loss lov - er touch - ing sev - en - ty four._____
tax - loss lov - er wears a crack - ing dress._____

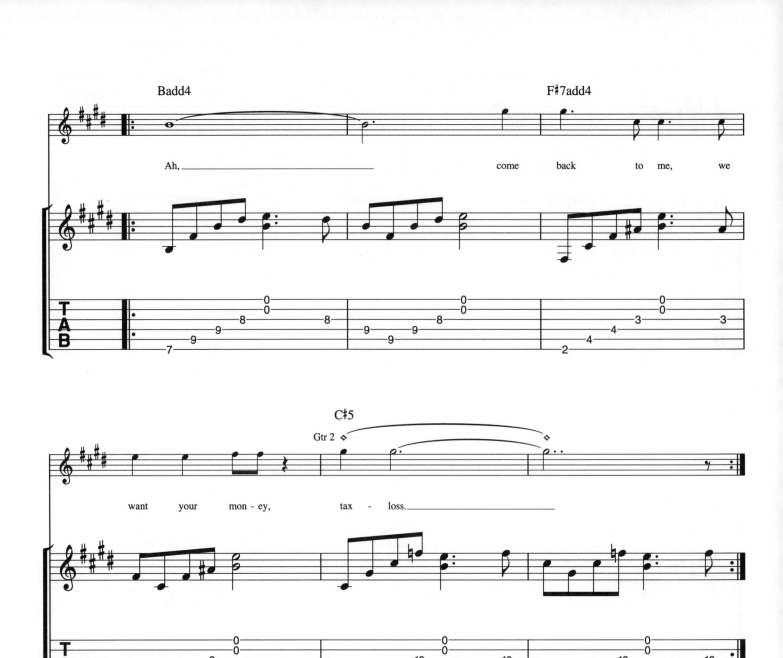

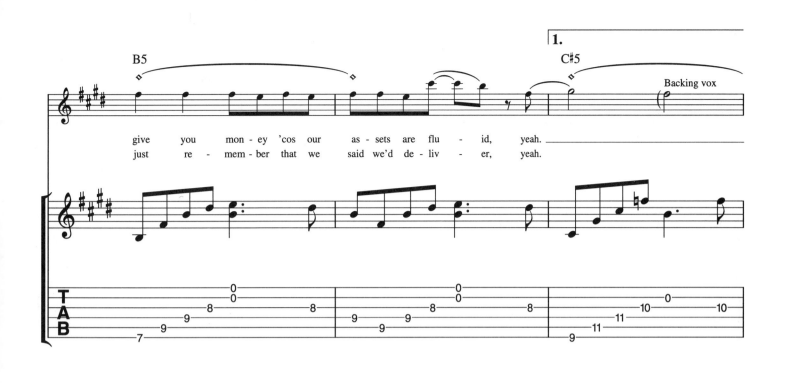

give you mon - ey 'cos our as - sets are flu - id, yeah.
just re - mem - ber that we said we'd de - liv - er, yeah.

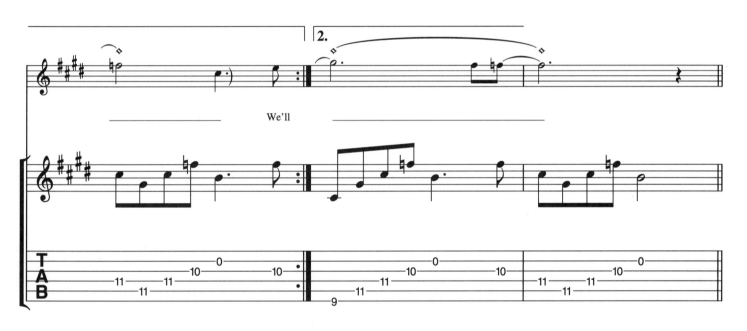

We'll

Sign ___ on the line ___ and we'll give you the mon - ey, and

then_____ you'll be mine_____ and we'll fly some - where sun - ny and you'll

quib - ble that our dri - vel seems un - sat - is - fac - tory, you're a tax loss._____
(we're)

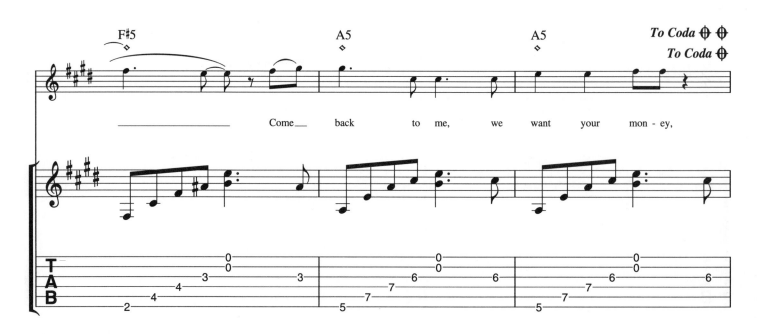

Come__ back to me, we want your mon - ey,

28

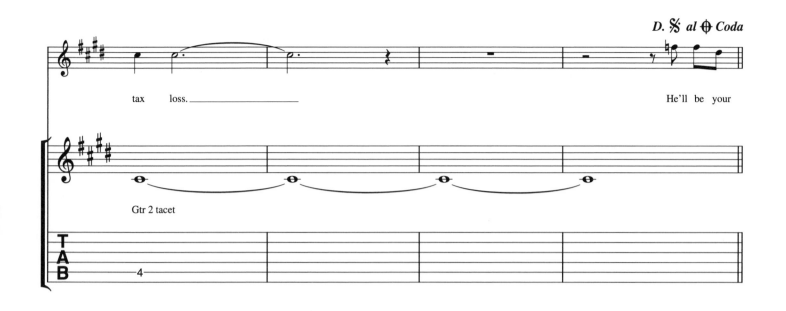

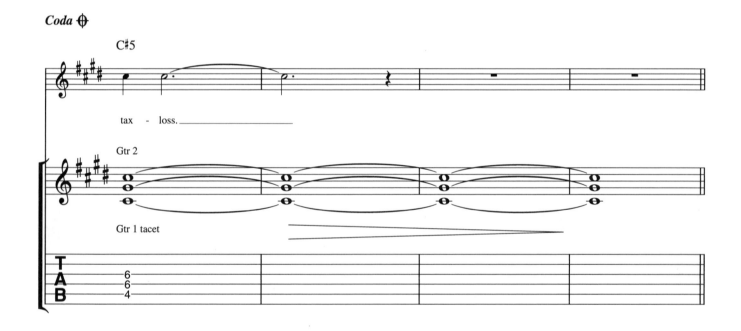

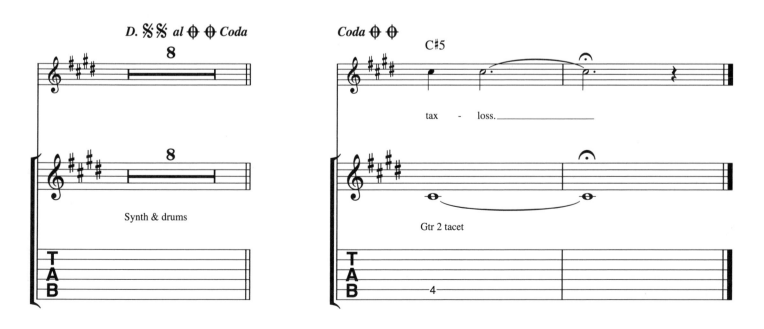

YOU, WHO DO YOU HATE?

WORDS & MUSIC BY PAUL DRAPER

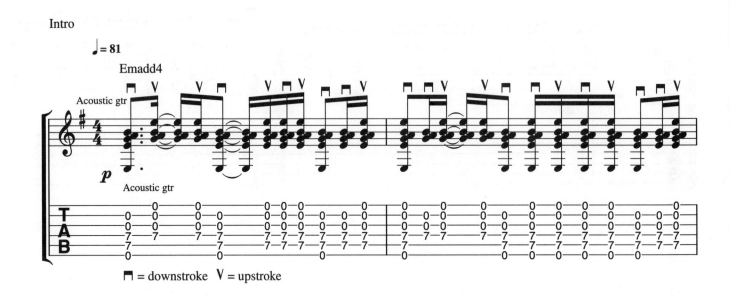

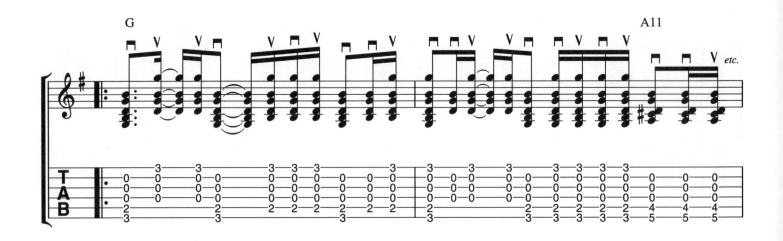

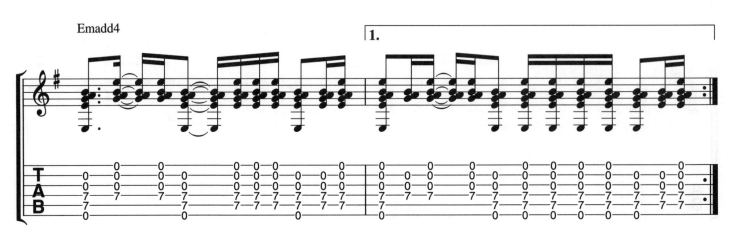

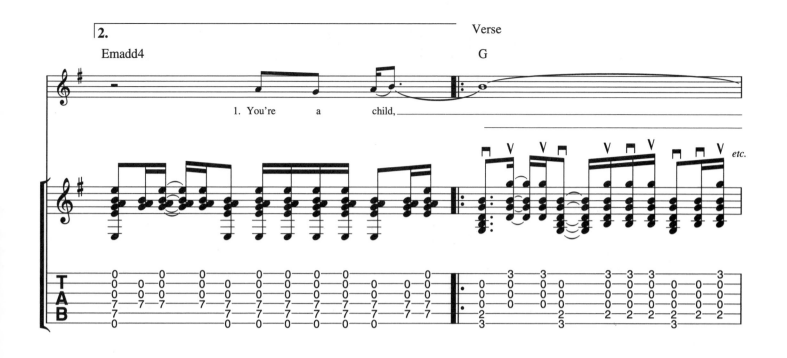

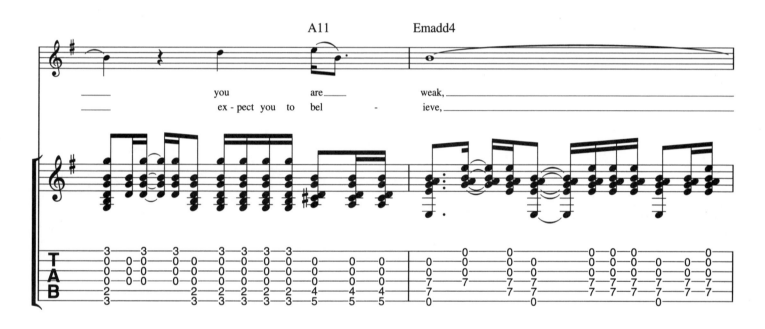

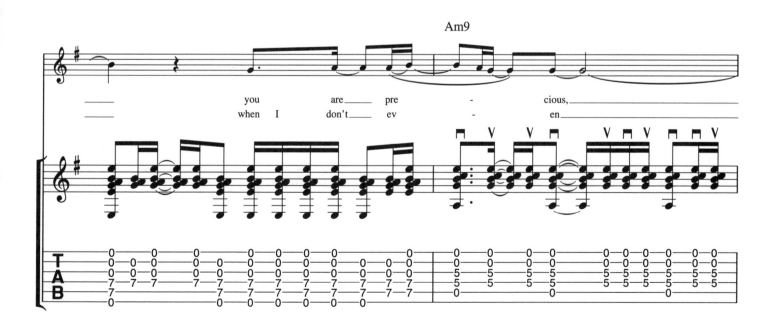

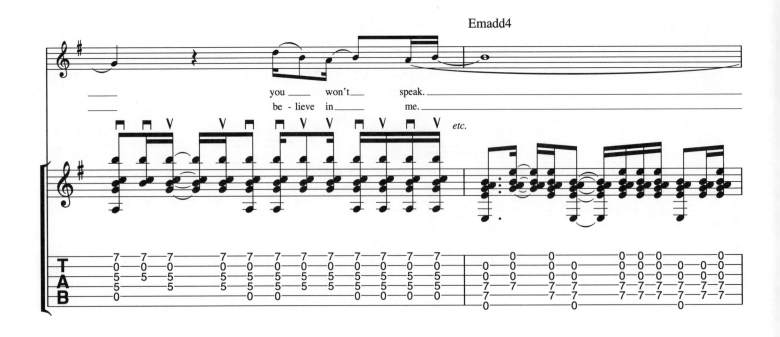

you _____ won't _____ speak. _____
be - lieve in _____ me. _____

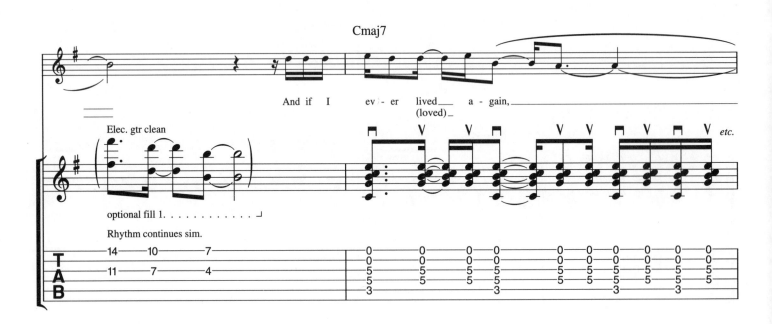

And if I ev - er lived _____ a - gain, _____
(loved) _____

Elec. gtr clean

optional fill 1. . . . .

Rhythm continues sim.

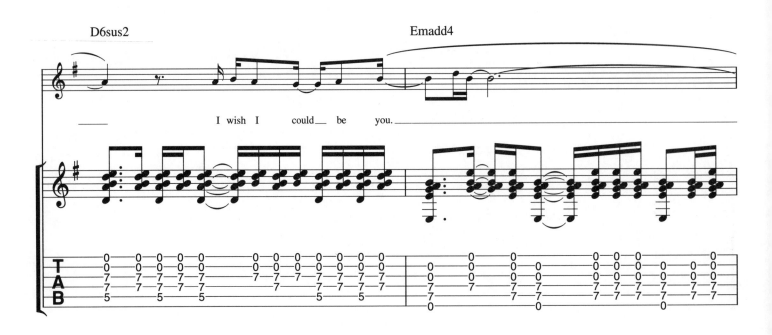

I wish I could _____ be you. _____

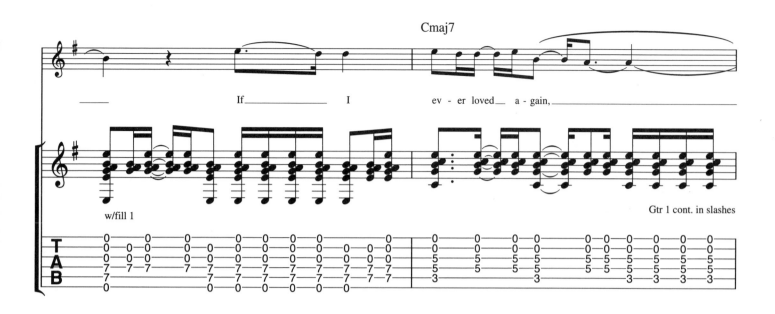

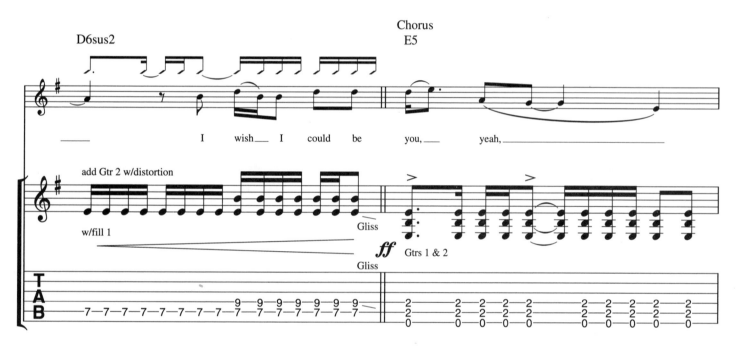

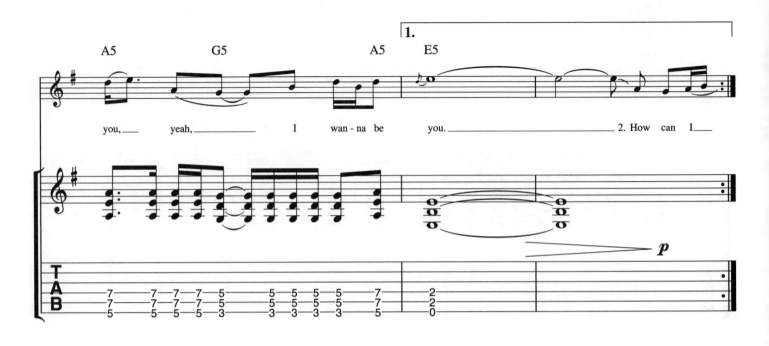

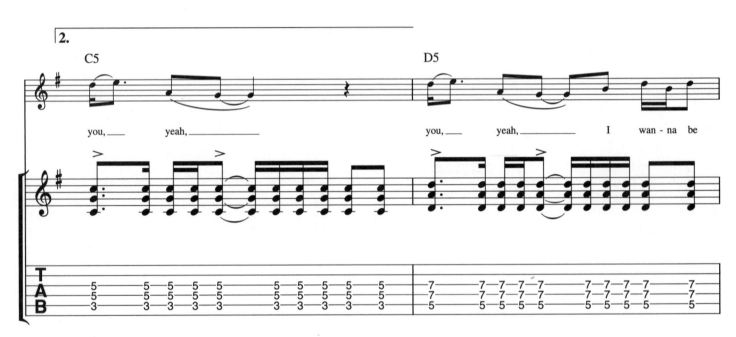

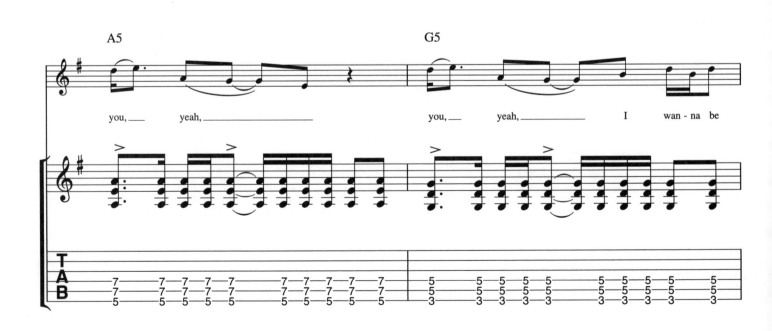

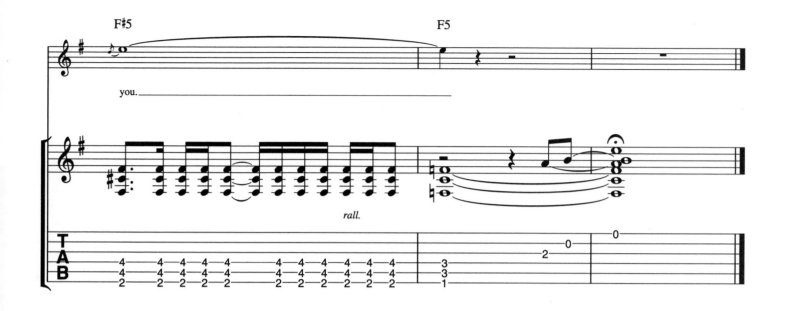

WIDE OPEN SPACE

WORDS & MUSIC BY PAUL DRAPER

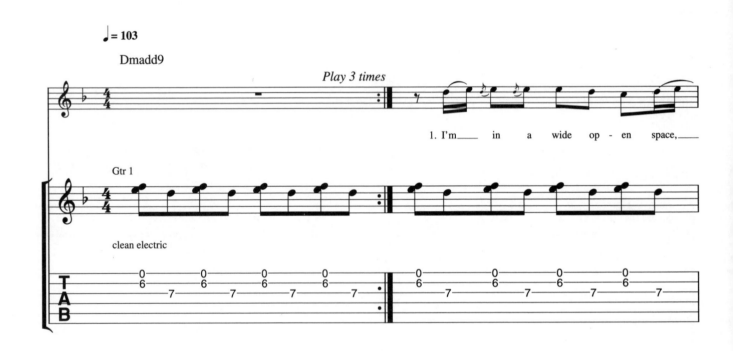

* end of solo, harmonic played at 3 1/3 fret on 3rd string

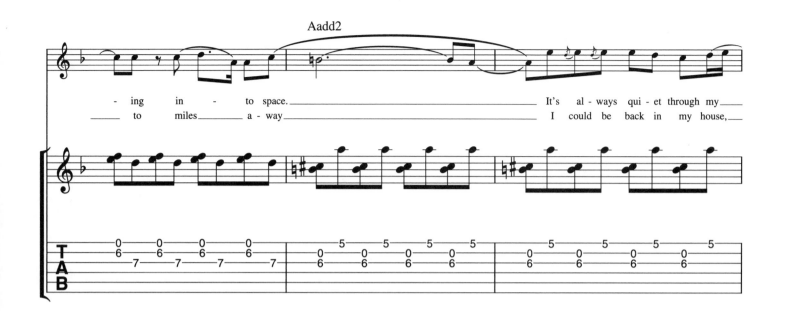

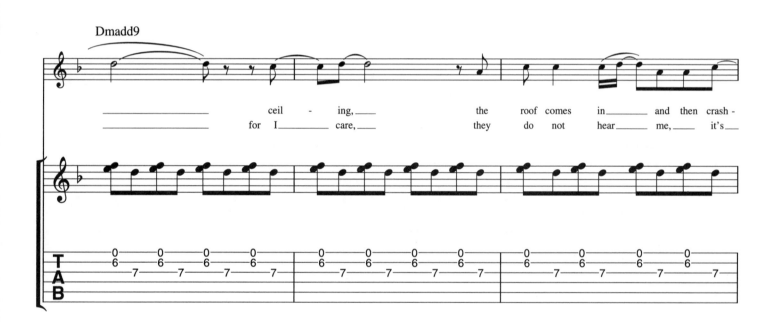

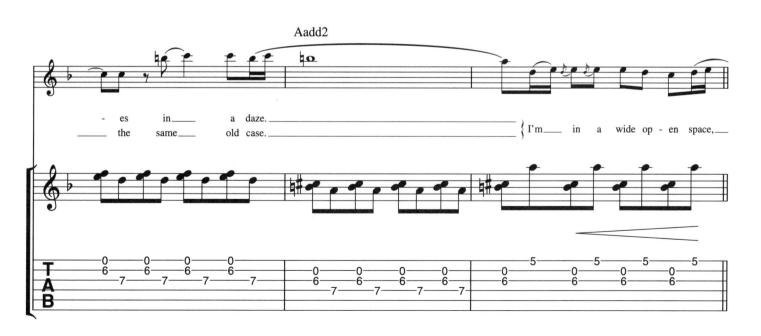

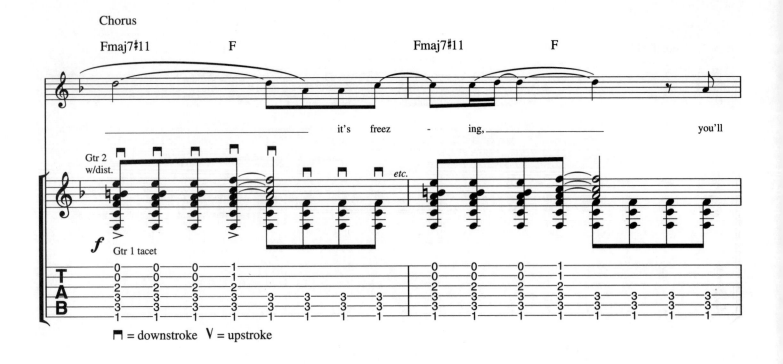

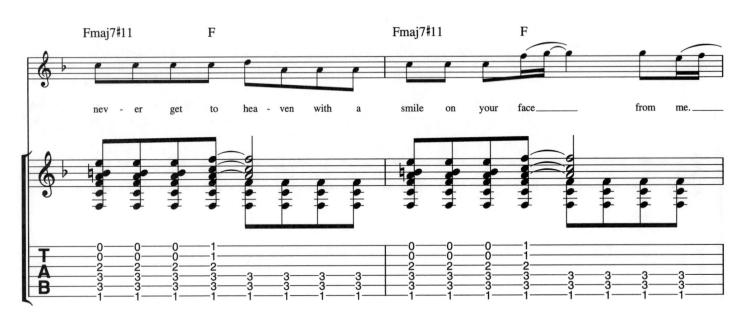

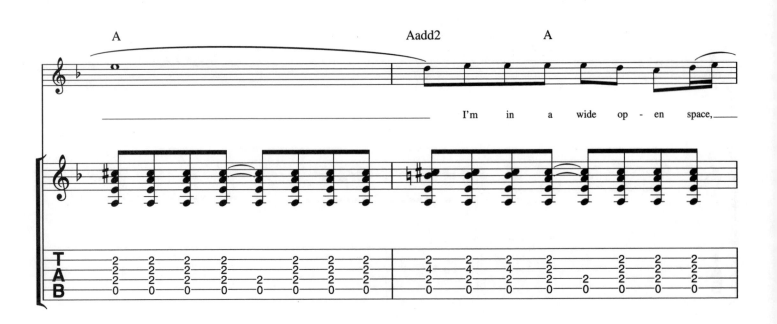

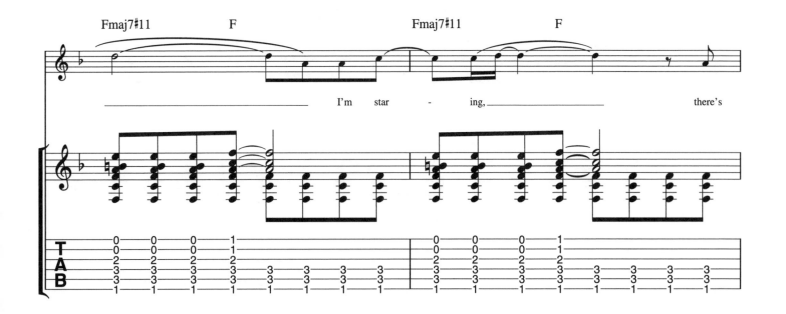

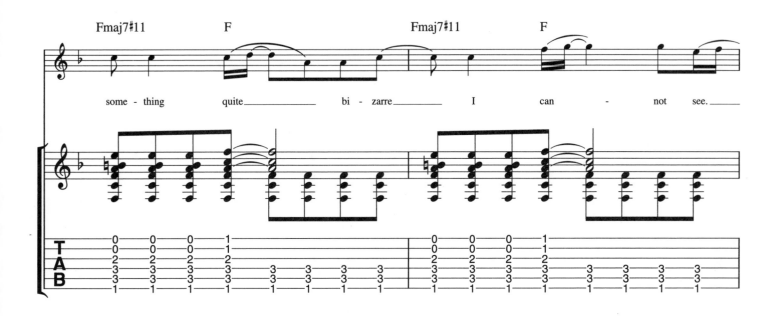

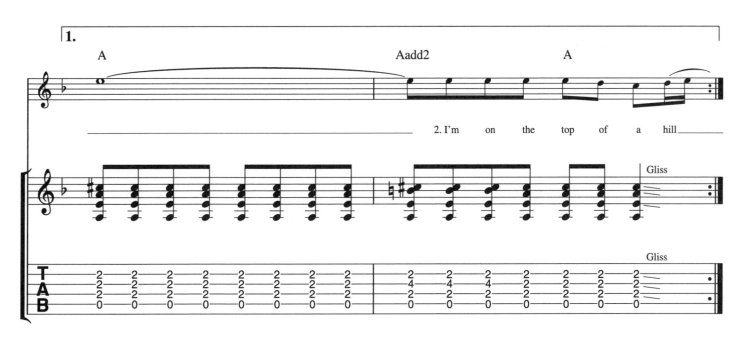

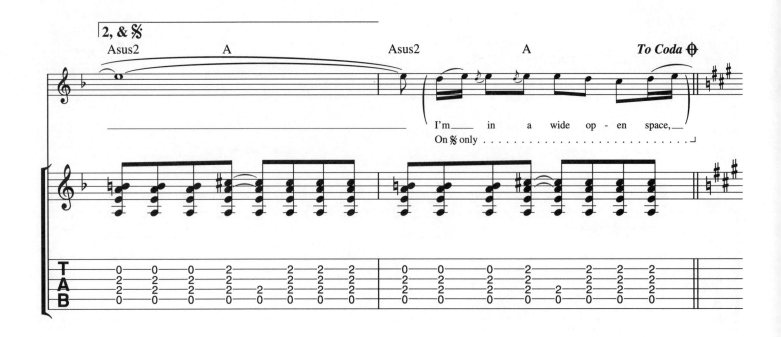

I'm___ in a wide op-en space,___
On % only . . . .

Solo

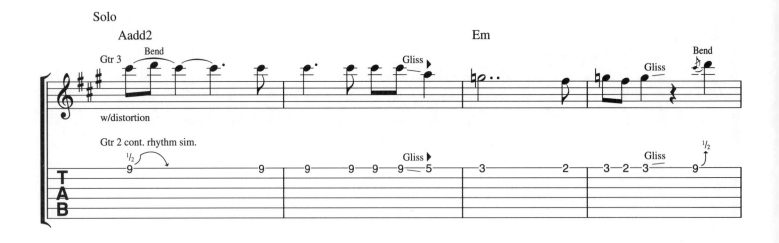

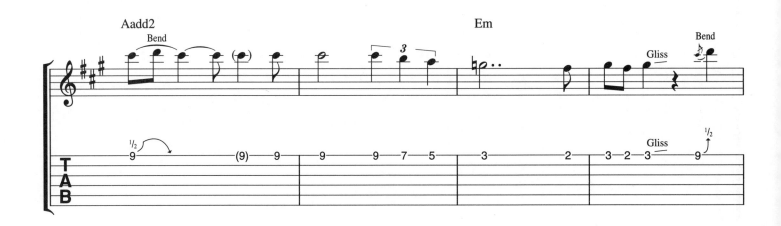

3. Wide op - en space,

41

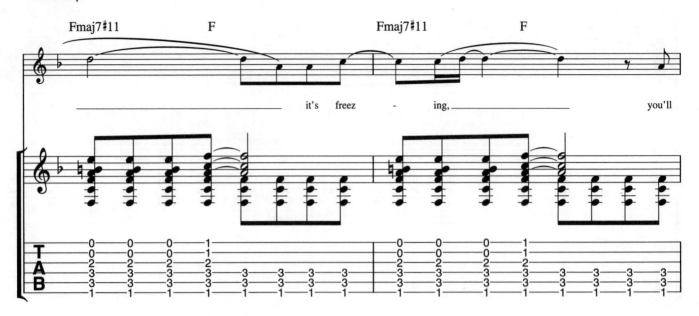

it's freez - ing, _____ you'll

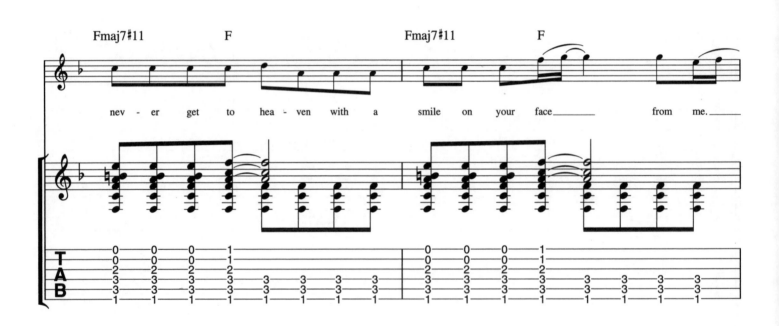

nev - er get to hea - ven with a smile on your face_____ from me._____

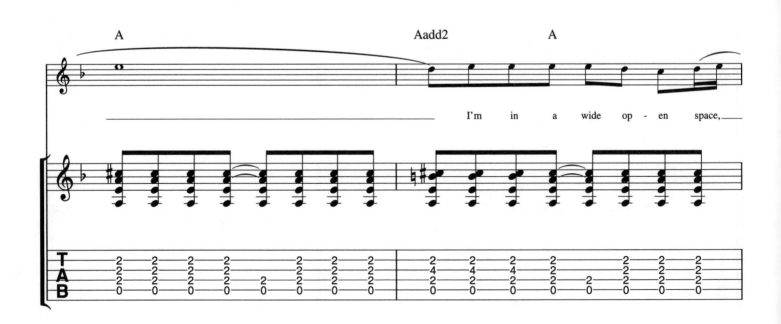

I'm in a wide op - en space,_____

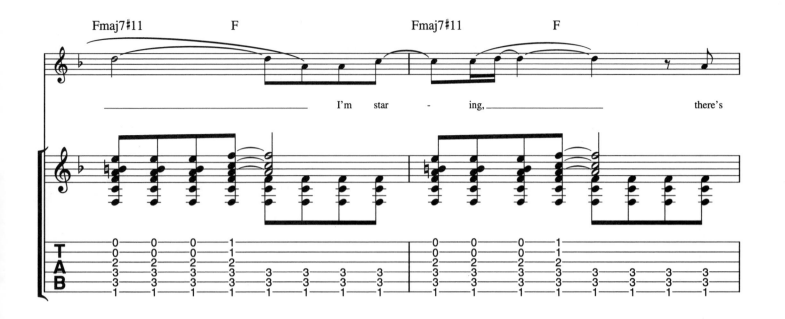

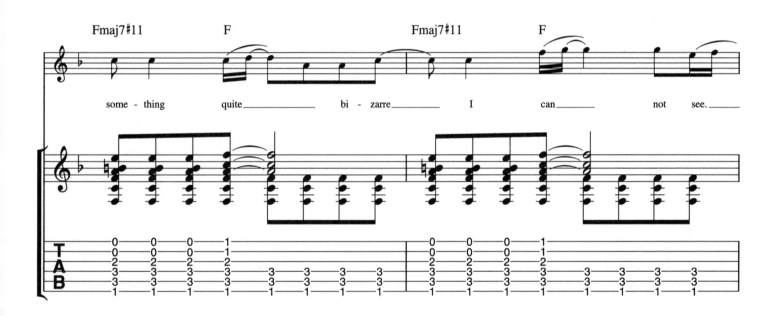

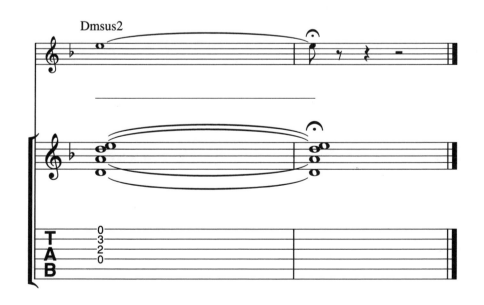

STRIPPER VICAR

WORDS & MUSIC BY PAUL DRAPER

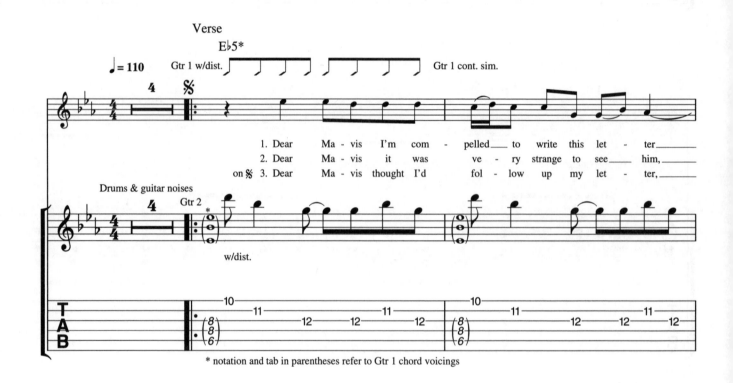

* notation and tab in parentheses refer to Gtr 1 chord voicings

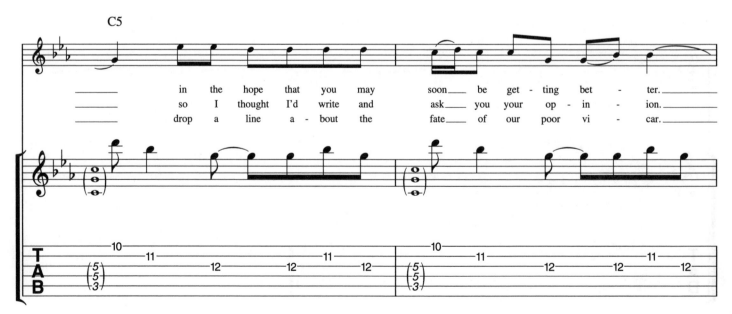

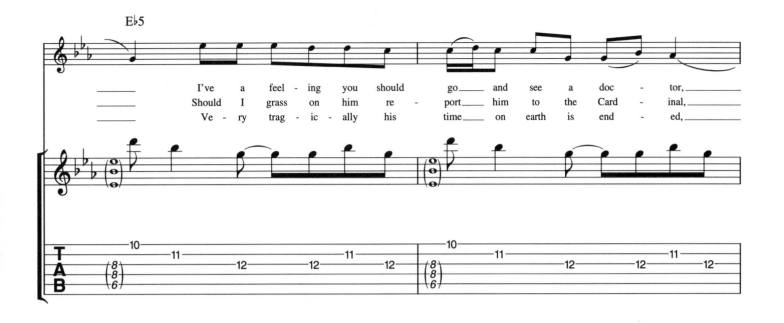

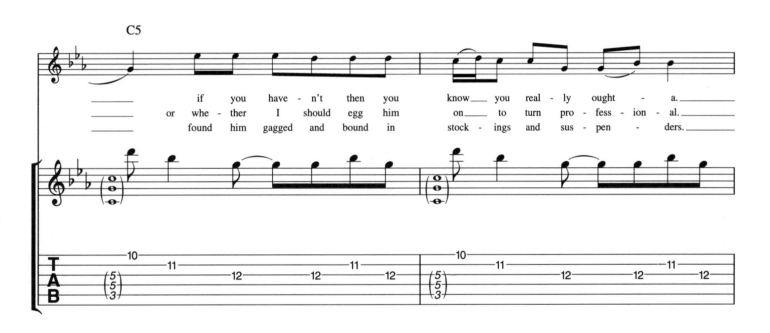

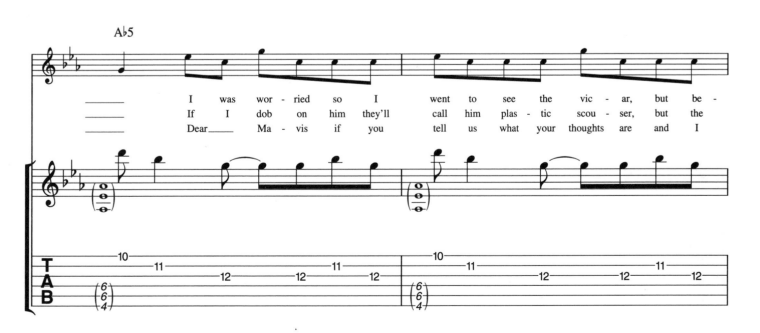

Chorus

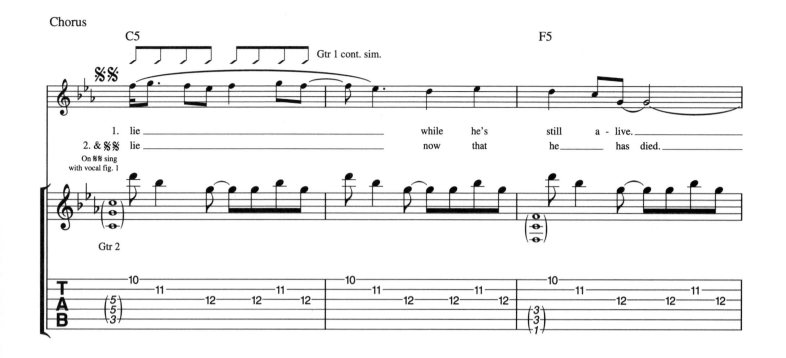

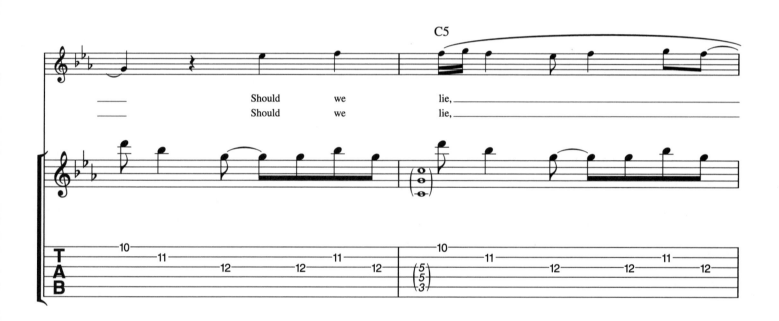

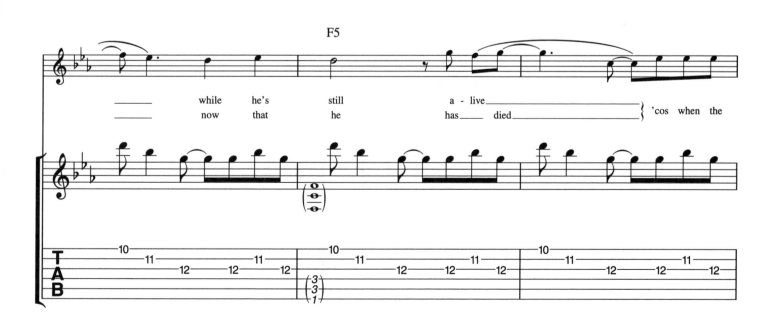

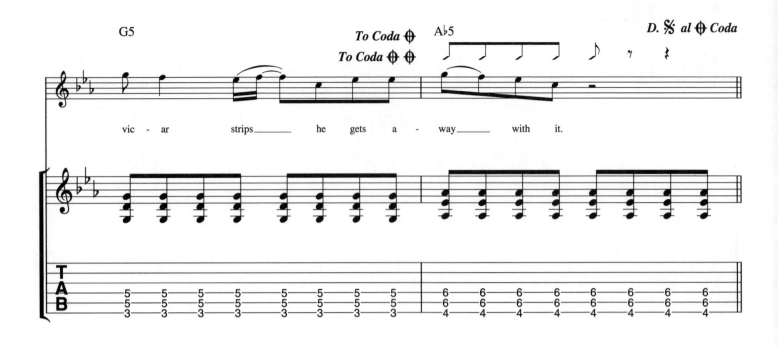

vic - ar strips_____ he gets a - way_____ with it.

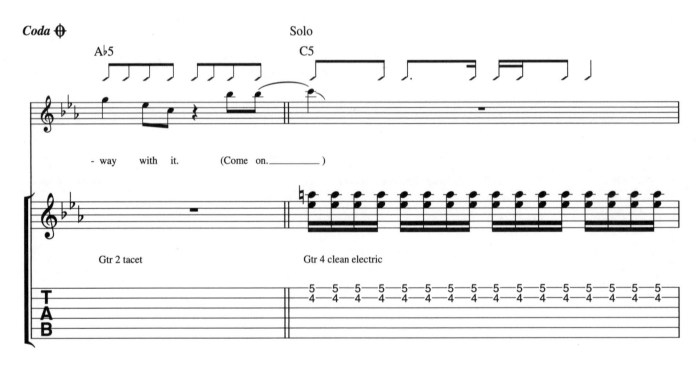

- way with it. (Come on._____)

Gtr 2 tacet

Gtr 4 clean electric

Gtr 1 cont. sim.

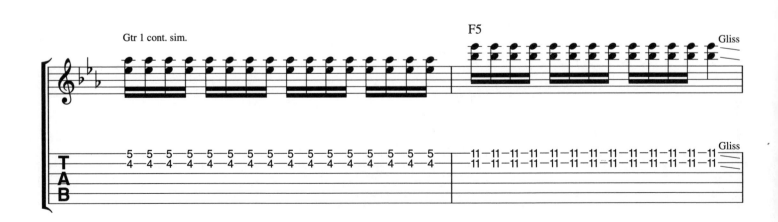

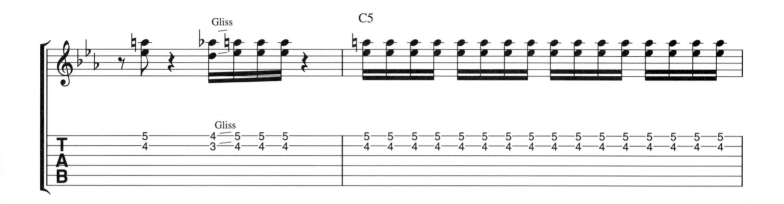

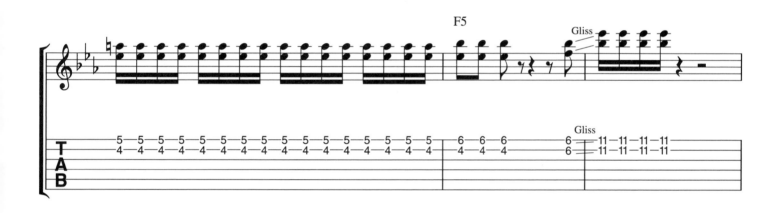

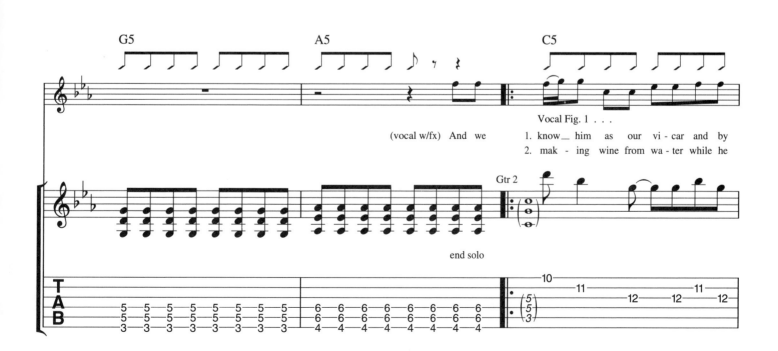

(vocal w/fx) And we

1. know__ him as our vi - car and by
2. mak - ing wine from wa - ter while he

Vocal Fig. 1 . . .

end solo

50

SHE MAKES MY NOSE BLEED

WORDS & MUSIC BY PAUL DRAPER

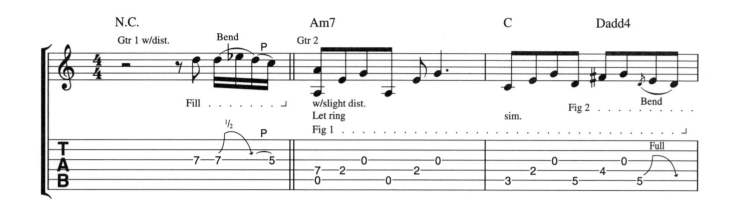

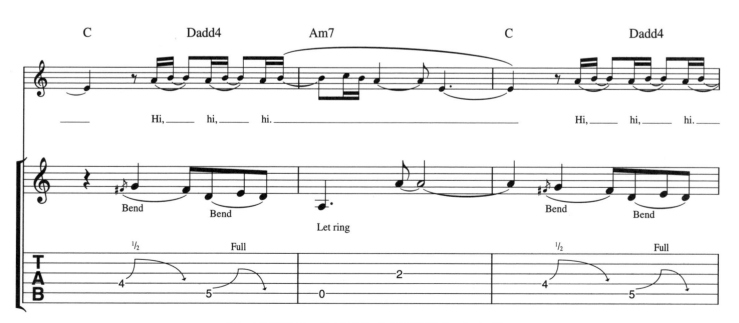

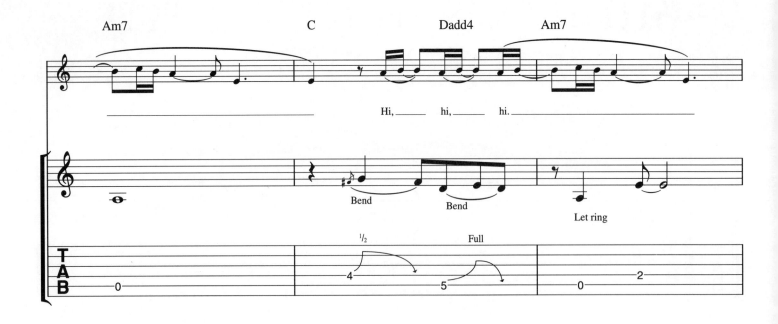

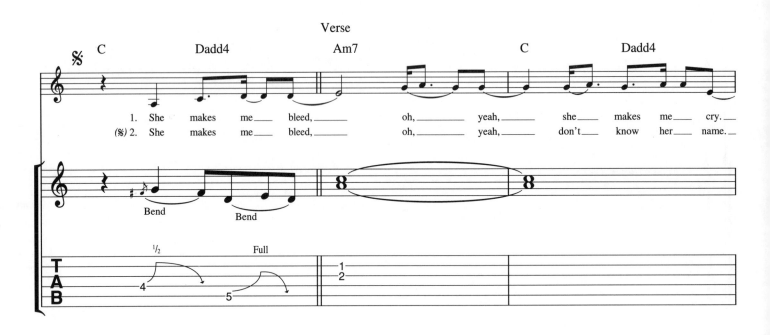

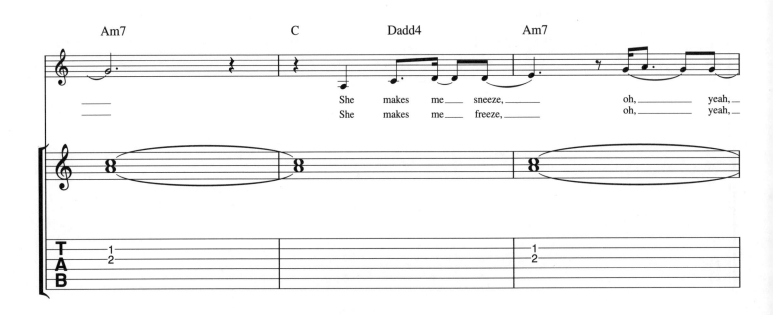

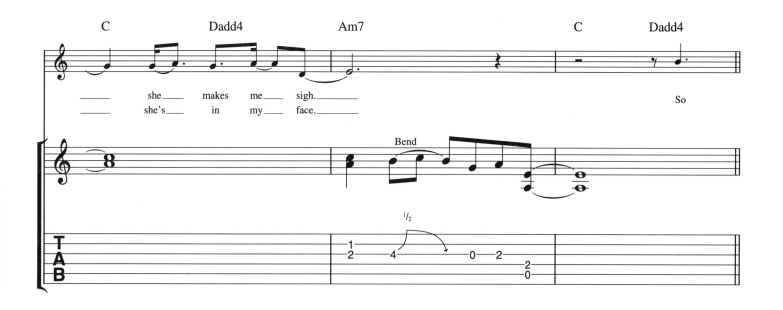

she___ makes me___ sigh.___   So
she's___ in my___ face.___

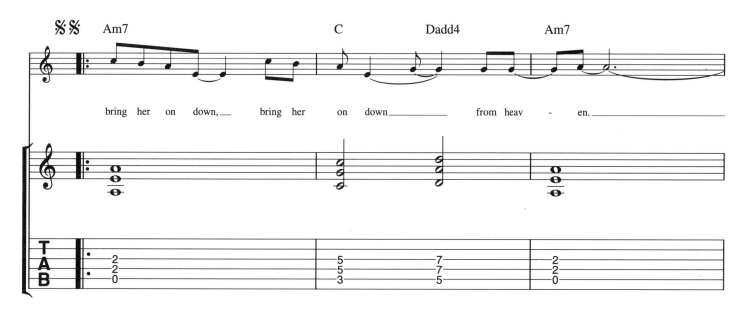

bring her on down,___ bring her on down___ from heav - en.___

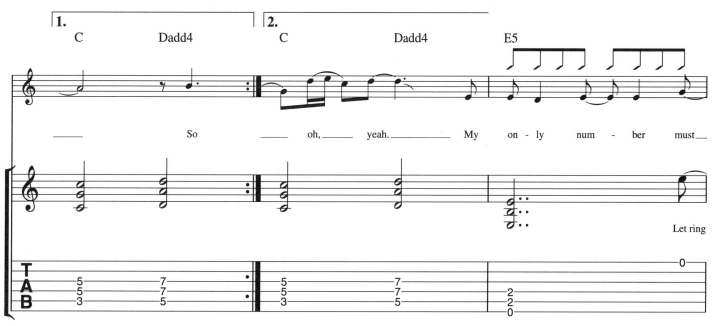

___   So   ___ oh,___ yeah.___ My on - ly num - ber must___

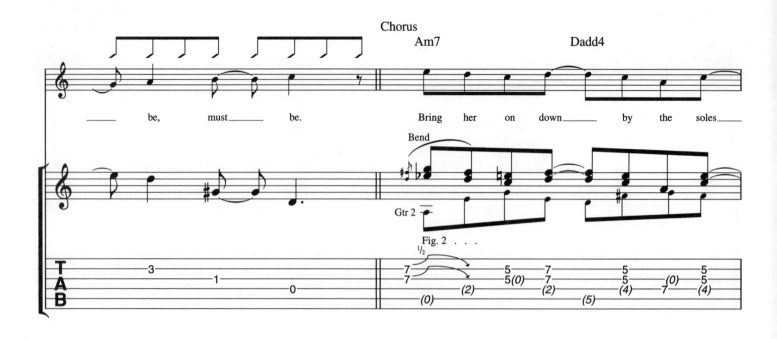

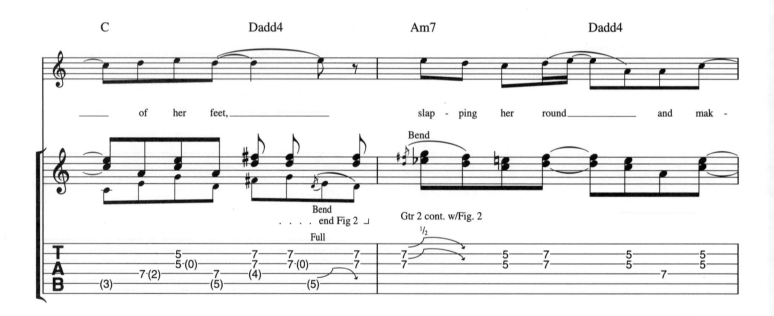

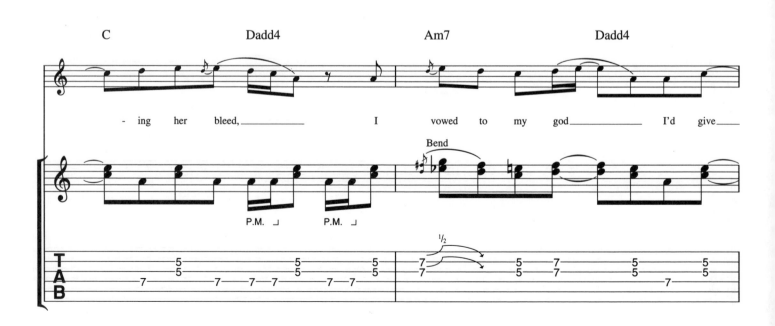

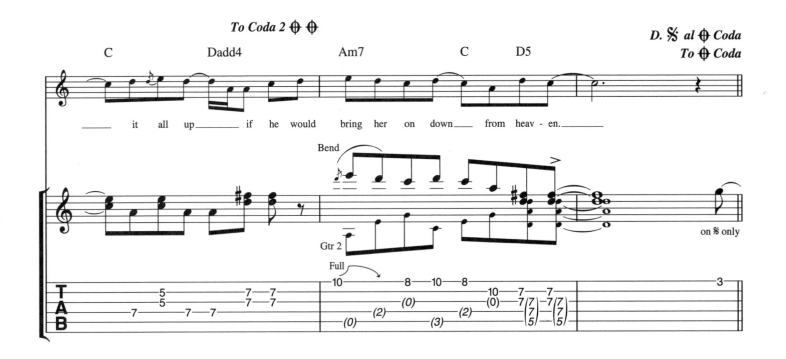

_____ it all up_____ if he would bring her on down_____ from heav - en._____

Bend

Gtr 2

Full

on 𝄉 only

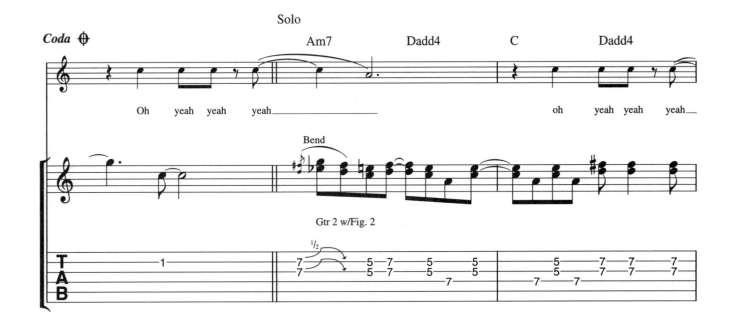

Coda ⊕

Solo

Oh yeah yeah yeah_____ oh yeah yeah yeah_____

Bend

Gtr 2 w/Fig. 2

1/2

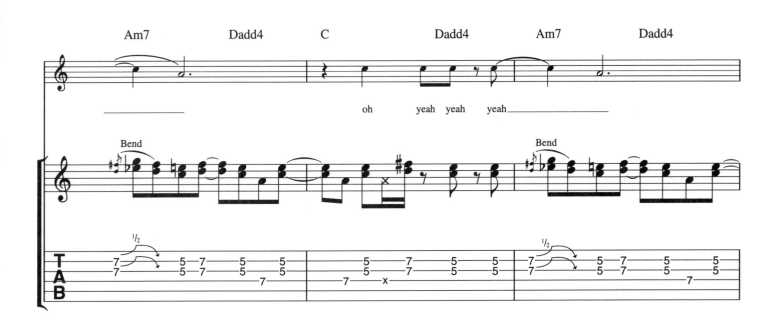

_____ oh yeah yeah yeah_____

Bend

Bend

1/2

1/2

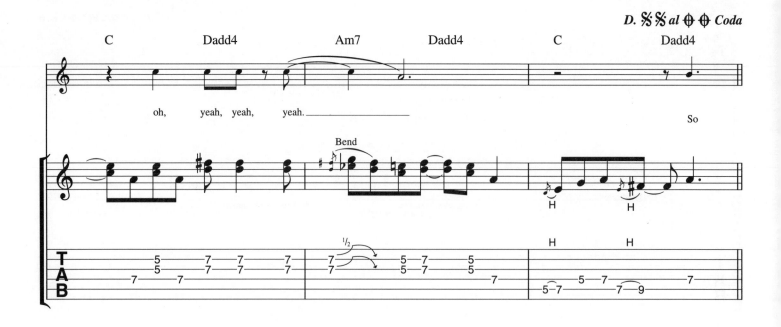

oh, yeah, yeah, yeah._____ So

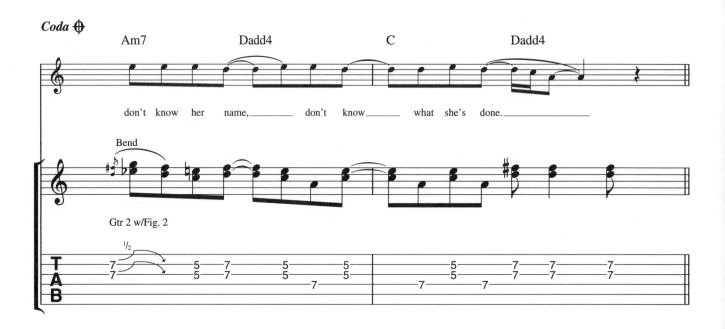

Coda ⊕

don't know her name,_____ don't know_____ what she's done._____

Gtr 2 w/Fig. 2

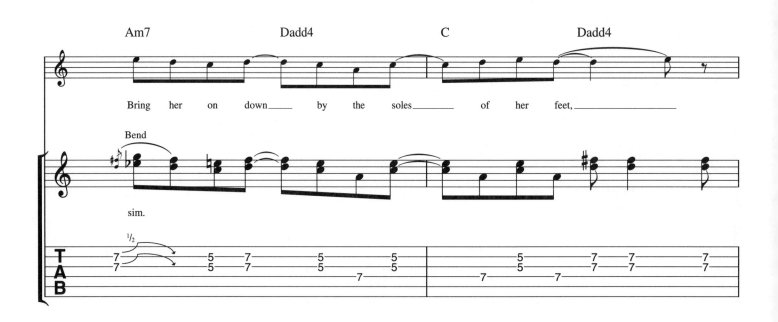

Bring her on down____ by the soles_____ of her feet,_____

sim.

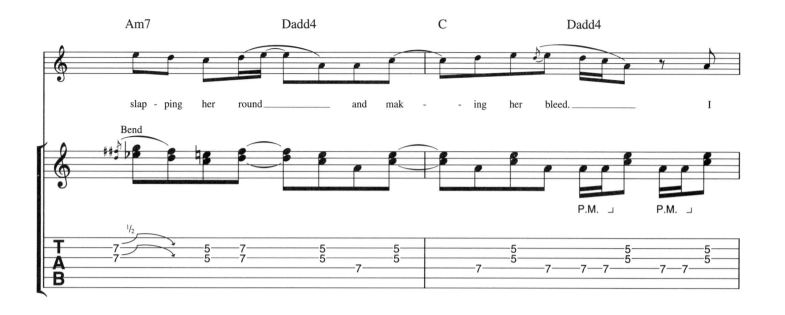

slap - ping her round_____ and mak - - ing her bleed._____ I

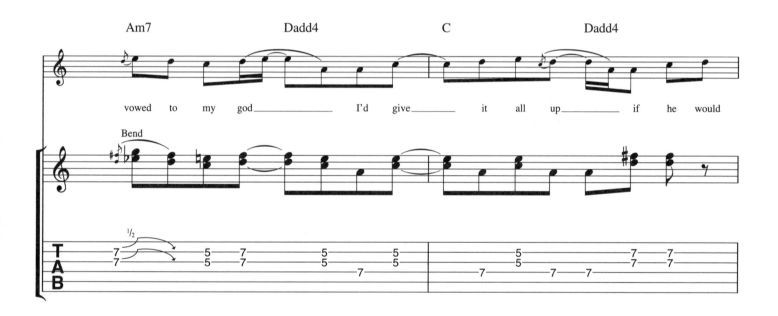

vowed to my god_____ I'd give_____ it all up_____ if he would

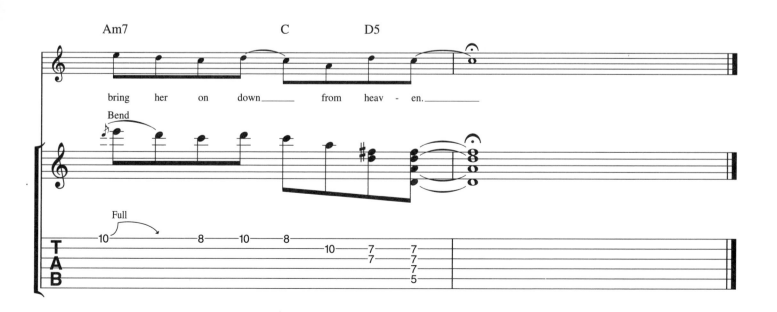

bring her on down_____ from heav - en._____

DISGUSTING

WORDS & MUSIC BY PAUL DRAPER

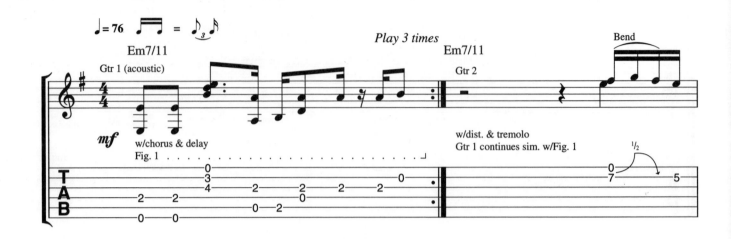

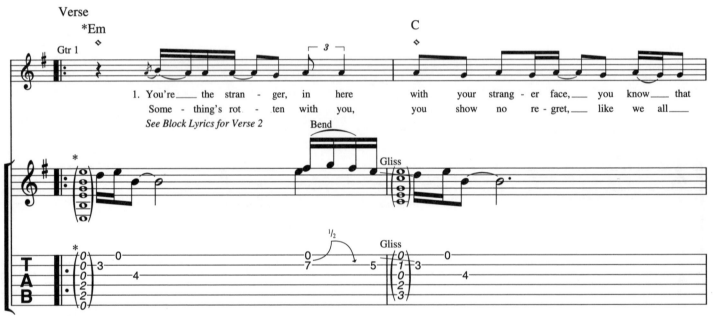

See Block Lyrics for Verse 2

1. You're___ the stran - ger, in here___ with your strang - er face,___ you know___ that
Some - thing's rot - ten with you, you show no re - gret,___ like we all___

* notation & tab numbers in parentheses refer to rhythm voicings

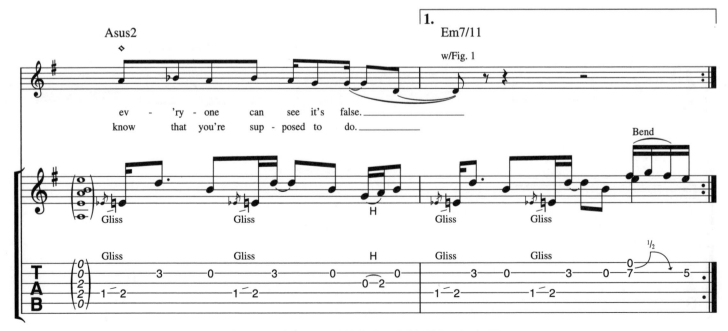

ev - 'ry - one can see it's false._____
know that you're sup - posed to do._____

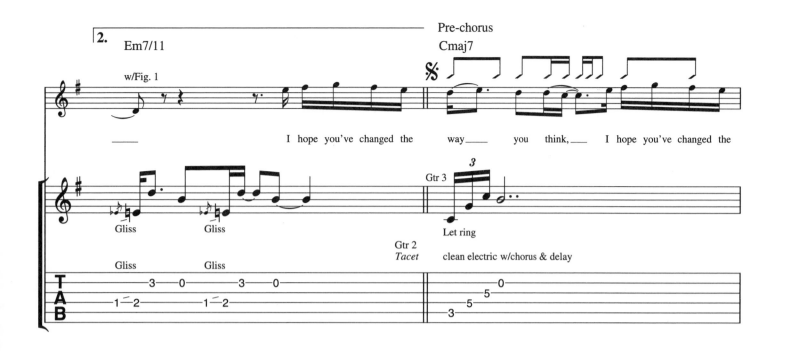

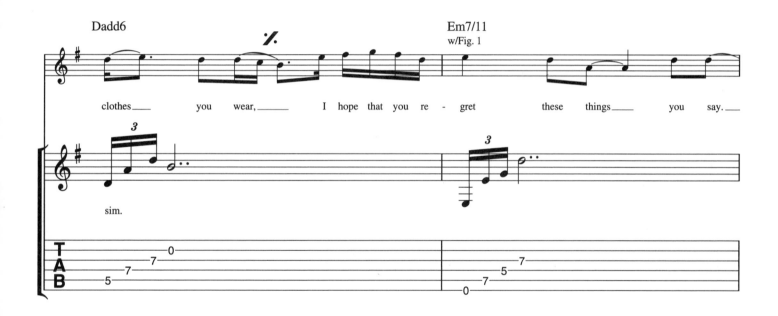

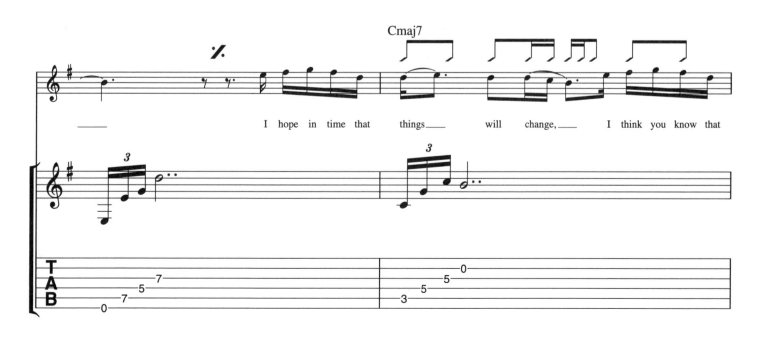

59

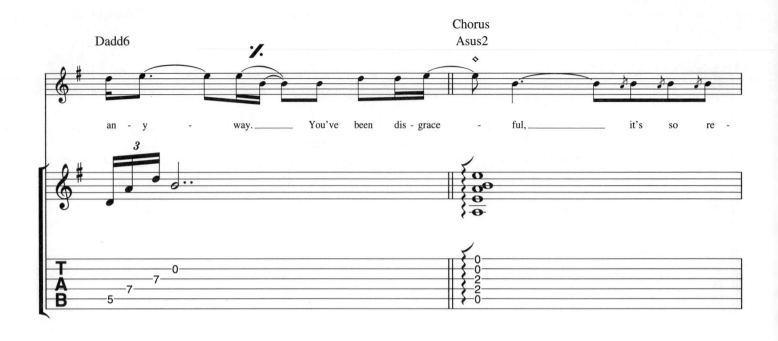

an - y - way. You've been dis - grace - ful, it's so re -

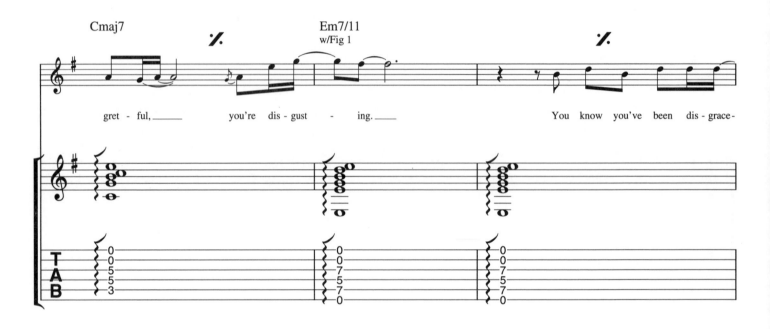

gret - ful, you're dis - gust - ing. You know you've been dis - grace -

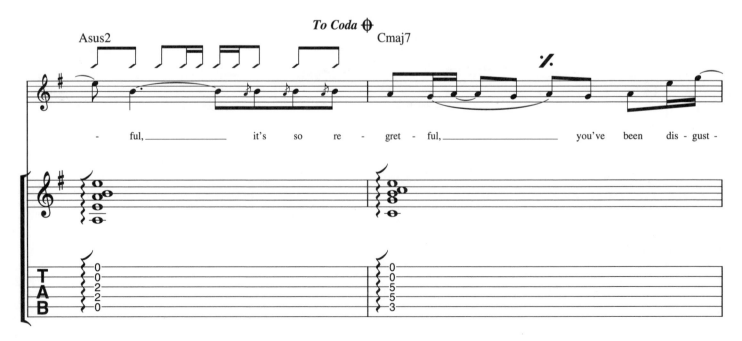

- ful, it's so re - gret - ful, you've been dis - gust -

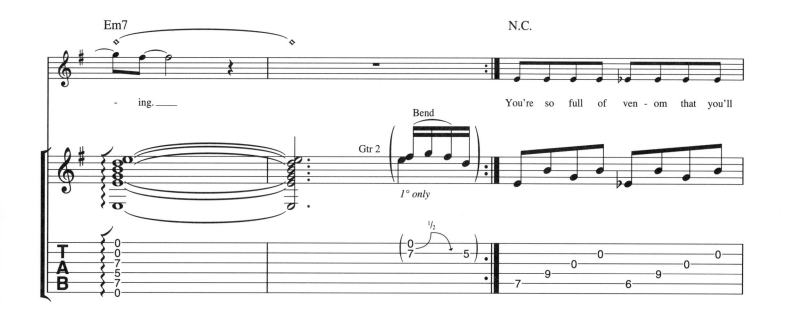

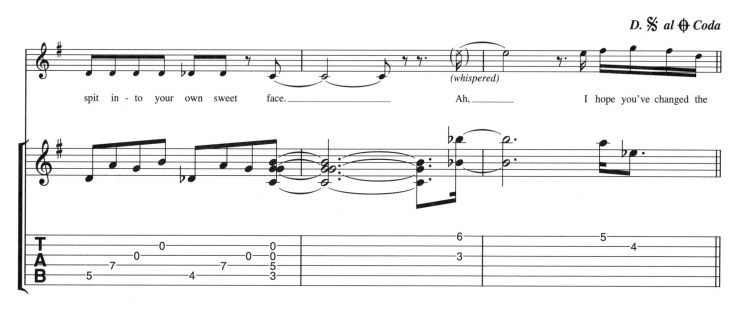

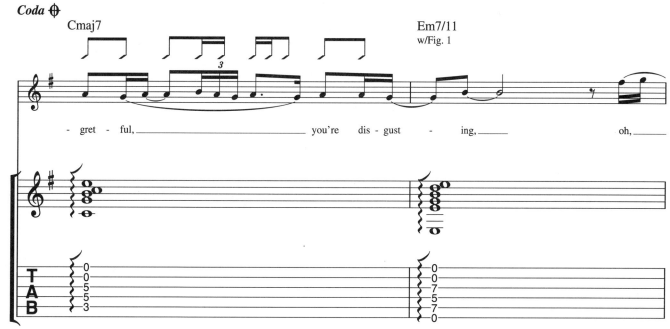

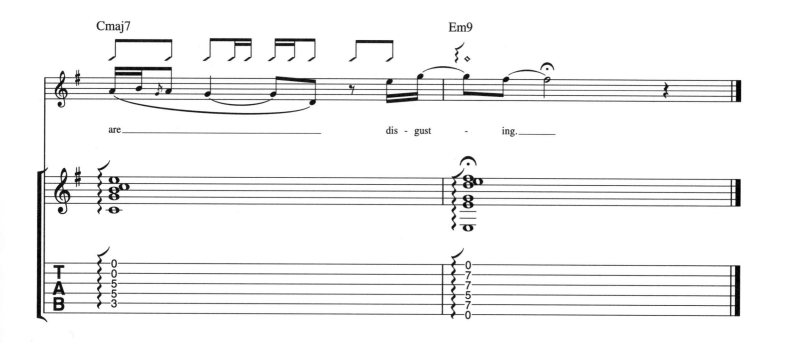

Verse 2

You're the outcast here
You're the native of a place
You've been and moved, excluded too
You create a tension
When we were the same
There was a pressure that would force you too.

NAKED TWISTER

WORDS & MUSIC BY PAUL DRAPER

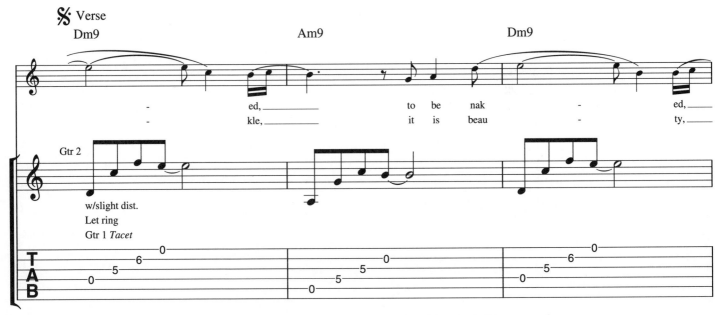

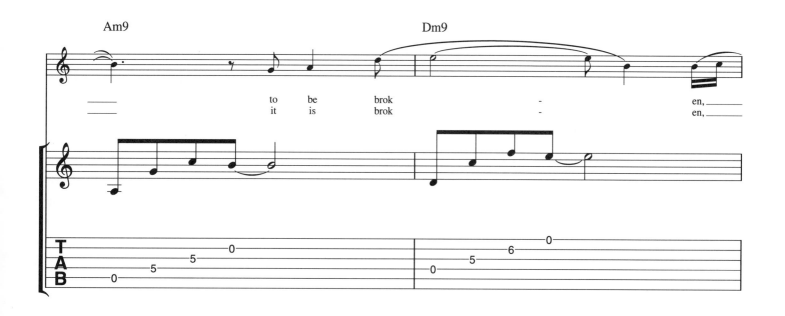

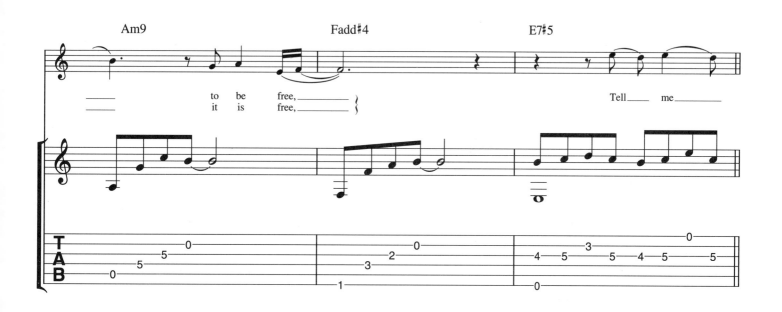

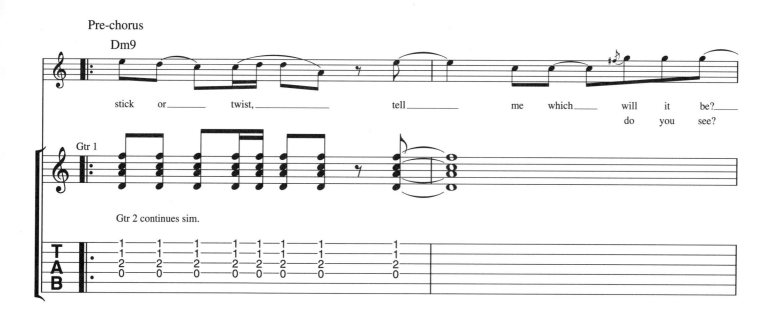

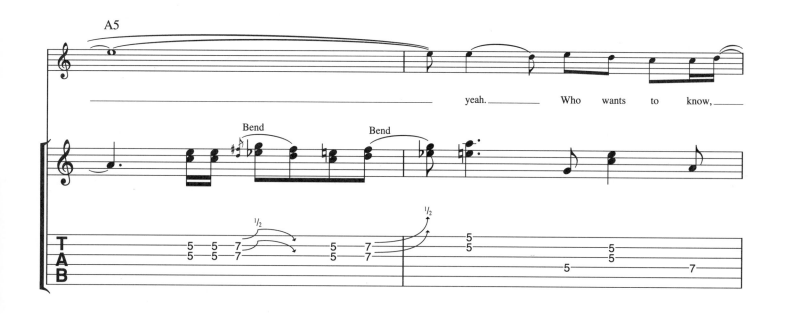

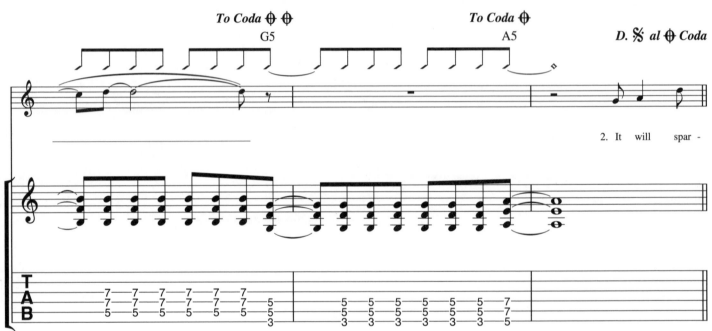

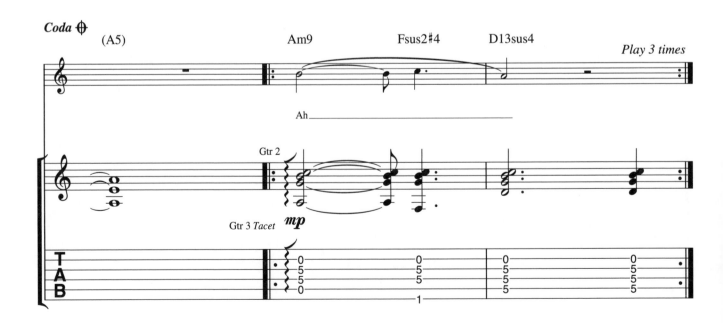

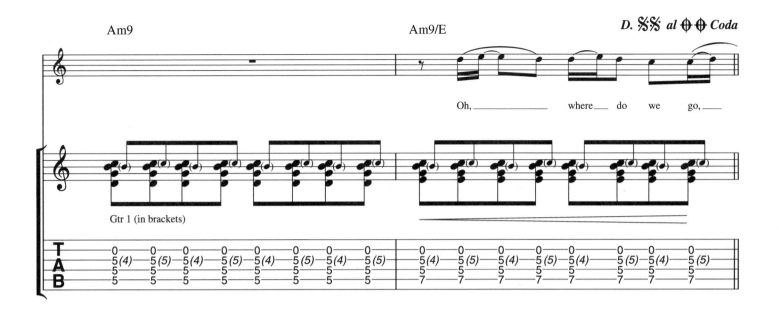

Oh,_____ where___ do we go,___

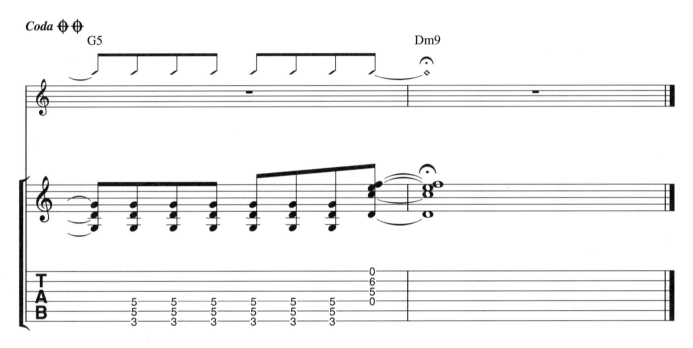

69

EGG SHAPED FRED

WORDS & MUSIC BY PAUL DRAPER

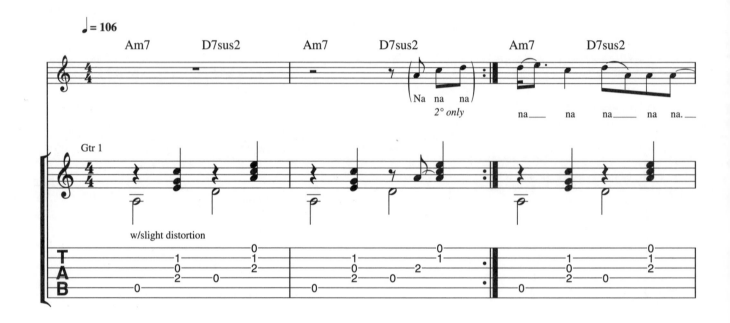

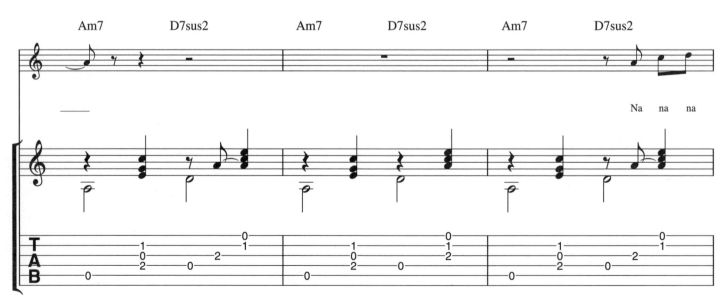

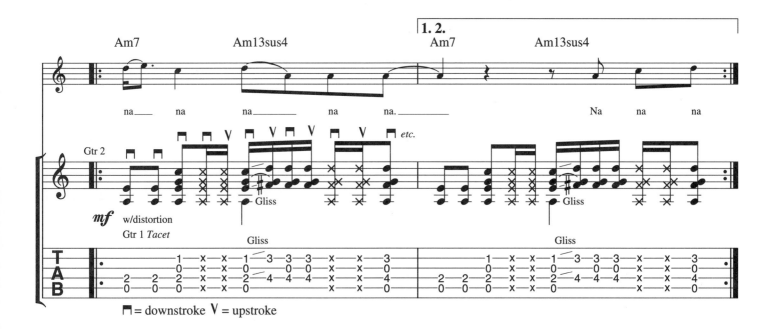

na____ na na_____ na na. Na na na

⊓ = downstroke **V** = upstroke

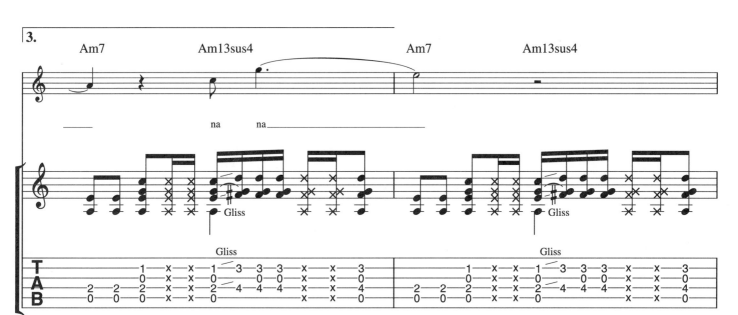

____ na na_____

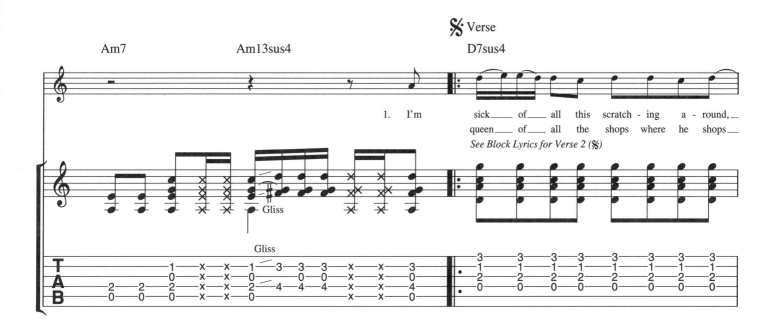

𝄋 Verse

1. I'm sick____ of____ all this scratch - ing a - round,____
queen____ of____ all the shops where he shops____
See Block Lyrics for Verse 2 (𝄋)

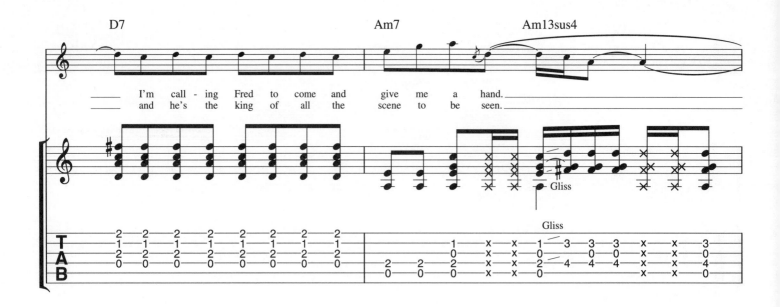

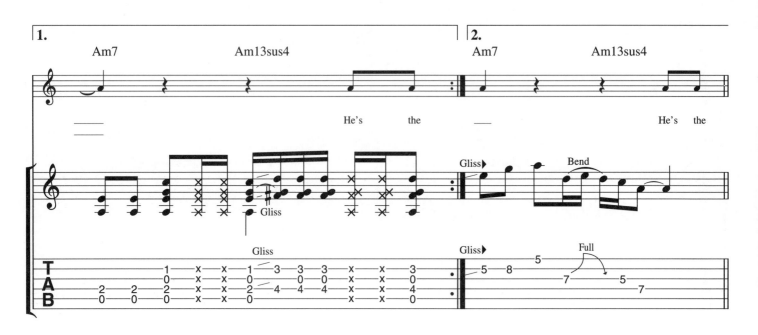

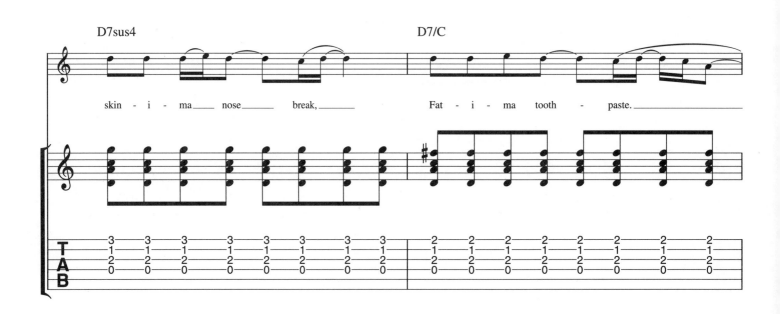

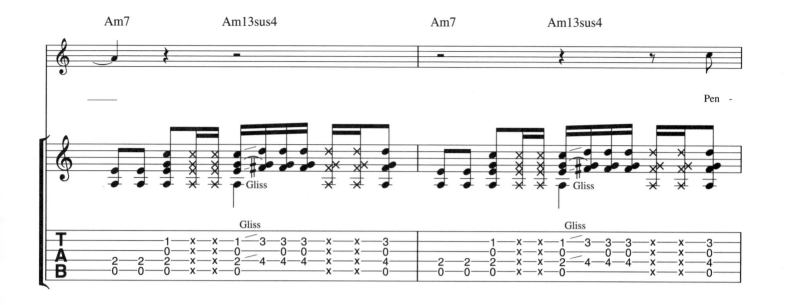

𝄋𝄋 Chorus

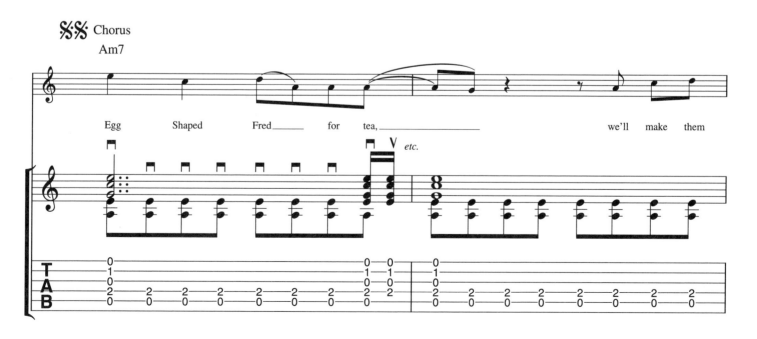

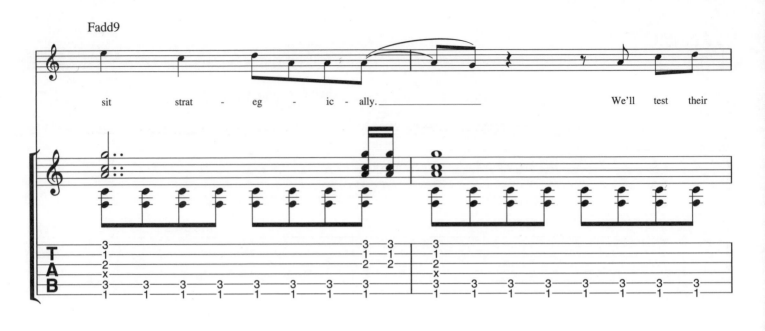

sit   strat - eg - ic - ally._____   We'll test their

To Coda ⊕
To Coda ⊕ ⊕

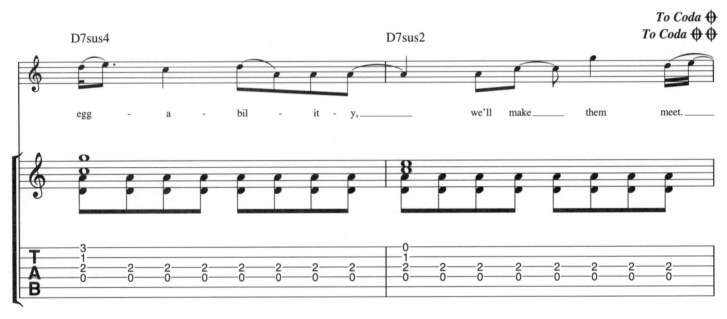

egg - a - bil - it - y,_____ we'll make_____ them   meet._____

D. 𝄊 al ⊕ Coda

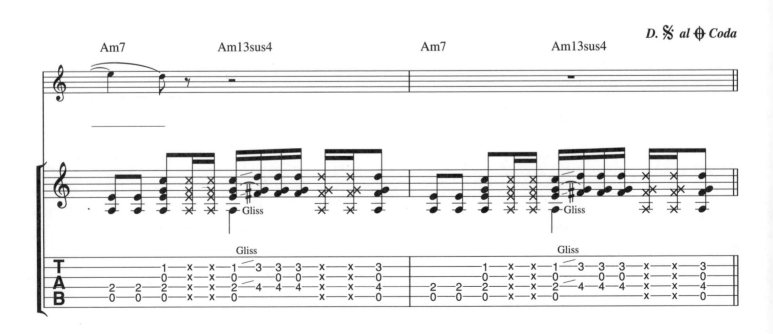

74

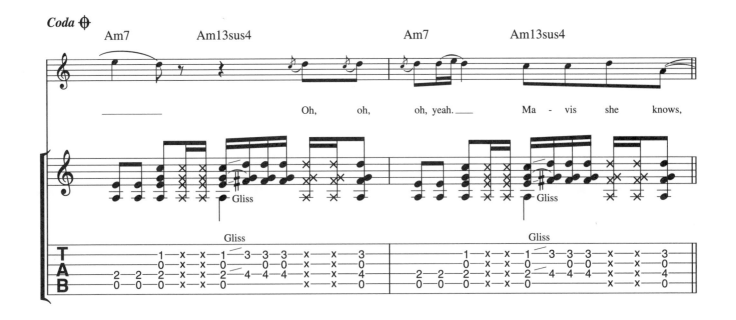

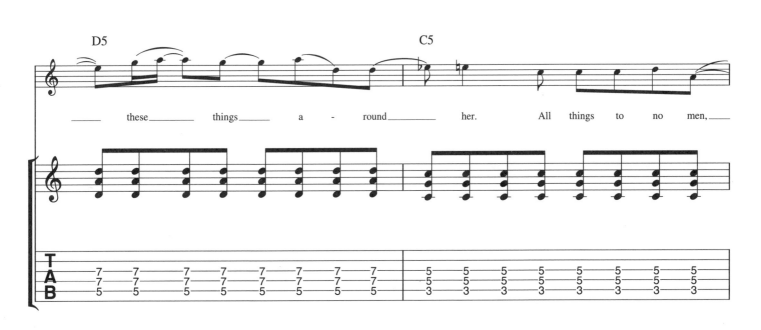

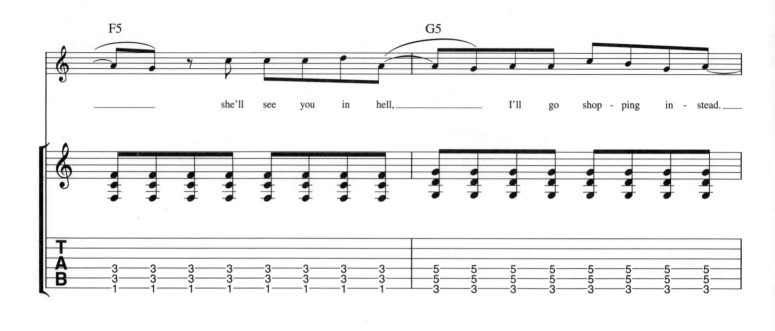

she'll see you in hell,_____ I'll go shop - ping in - stead.____

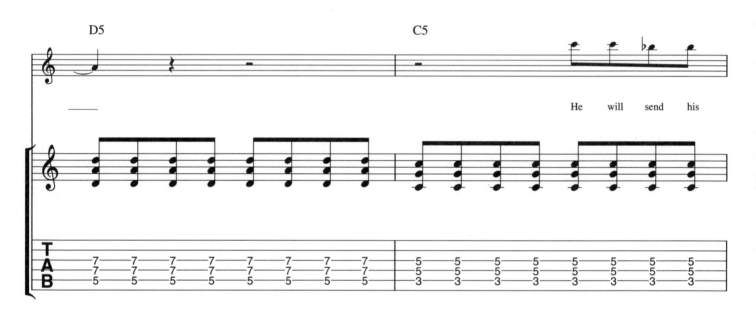

He will send his

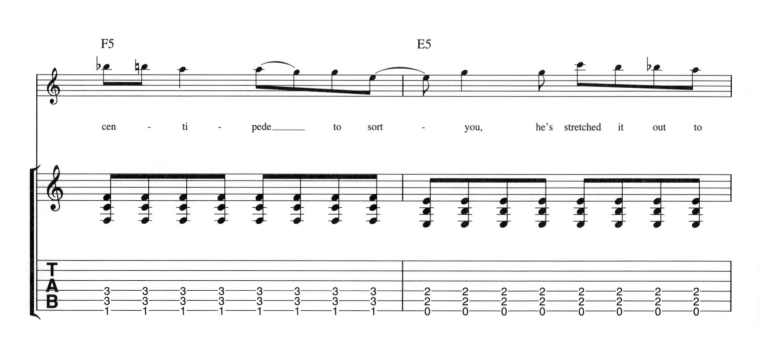

cen - ti - pede_____ to sort - you, he's stretched it out to

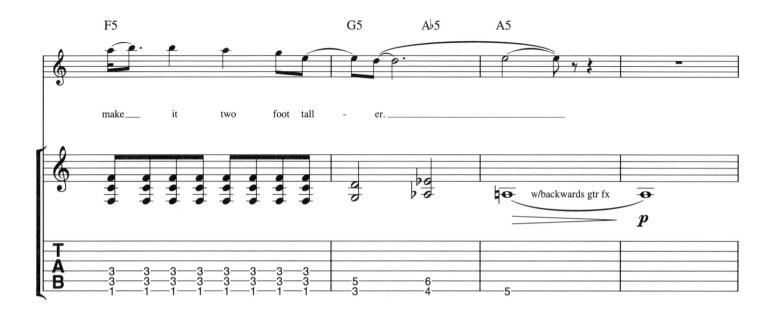

make___ it two foot tall - er._____

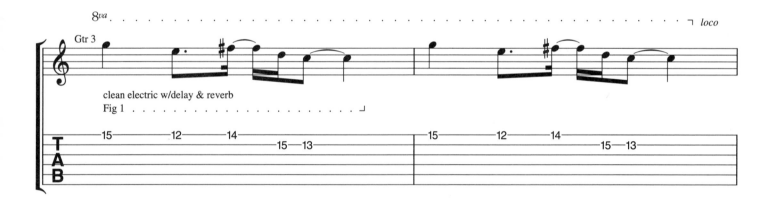

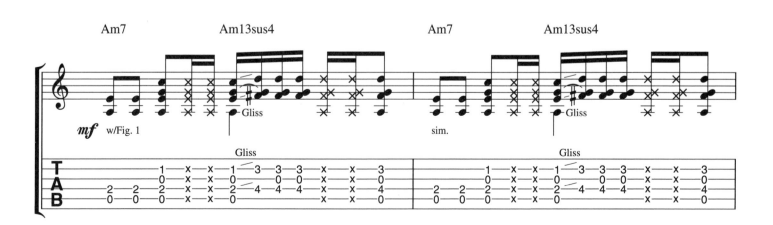

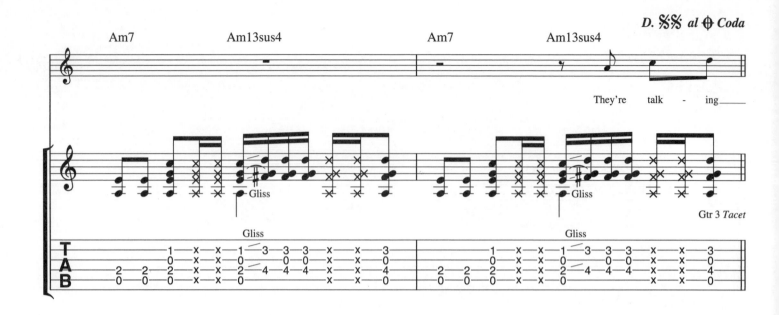

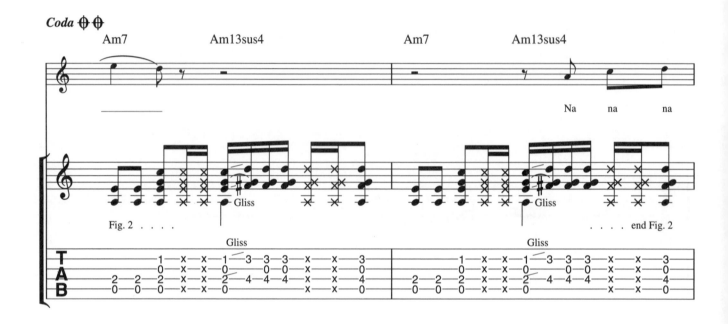

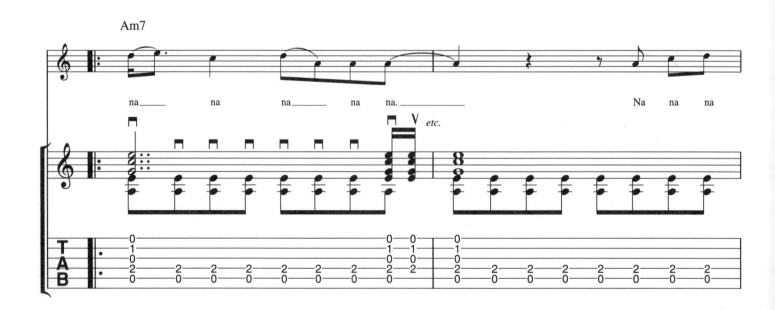

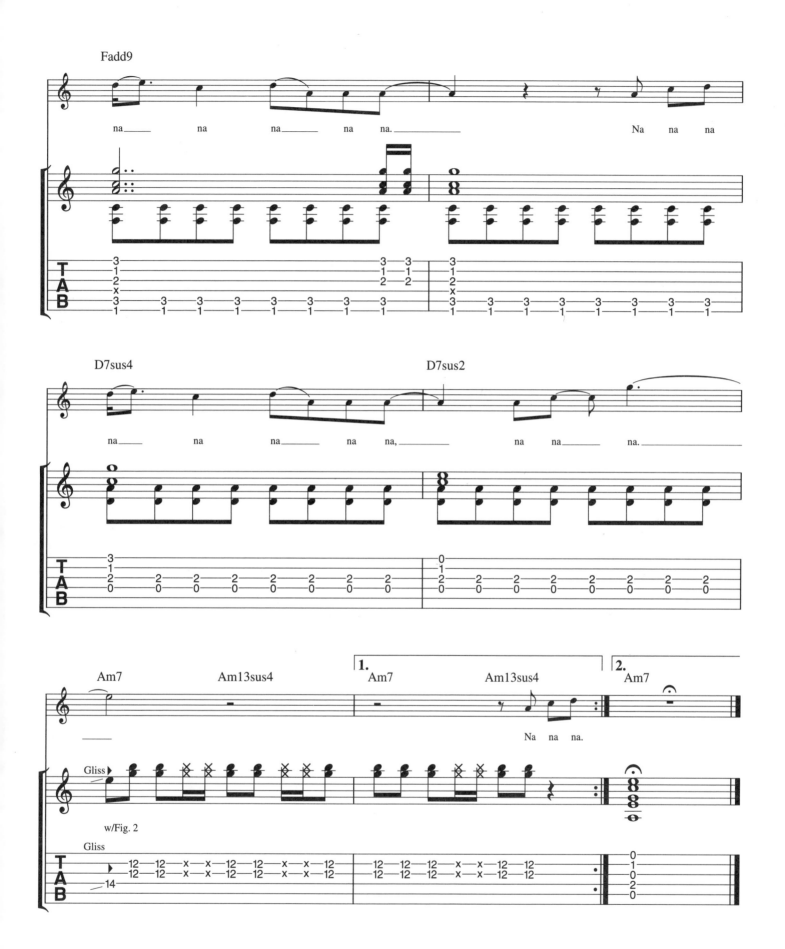

Verse 2 (%)   He only wants to get in your kecks
So he can carry out his own little test
He only wants to get in your pants
Because he knows that you've played in a band.

DARK MAVIS

WORDS & MUSIC BY PAUL DRAPER

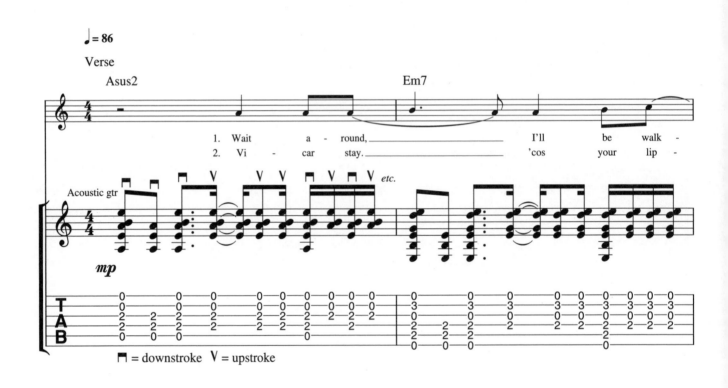

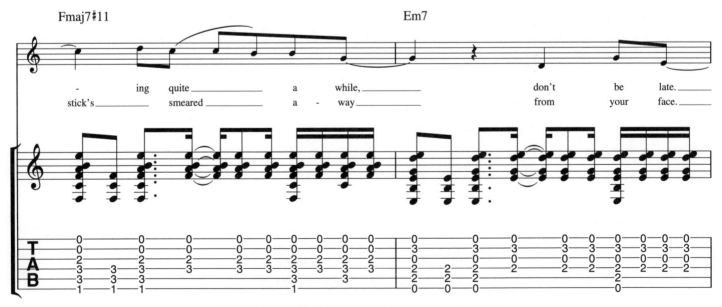

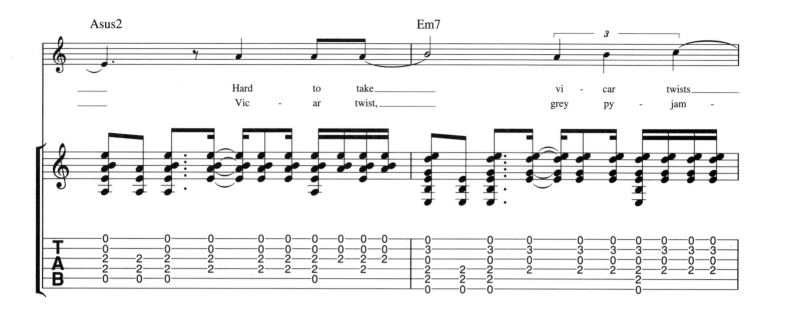

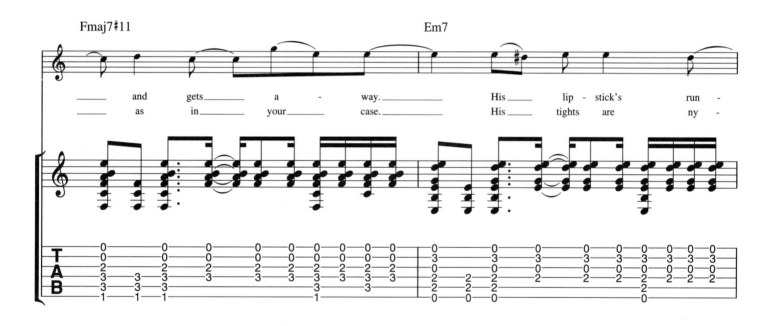

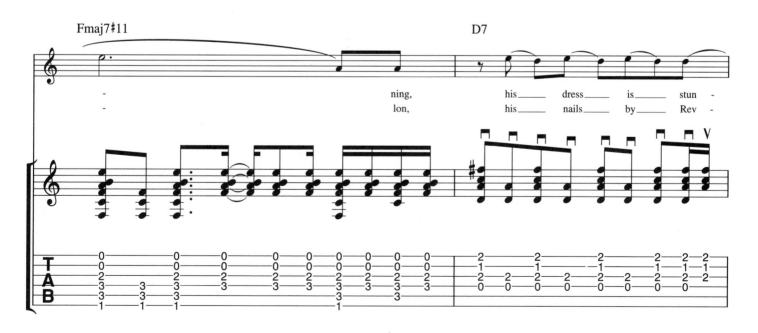

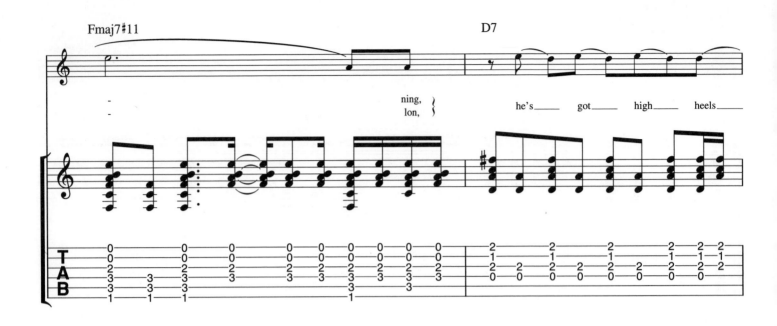

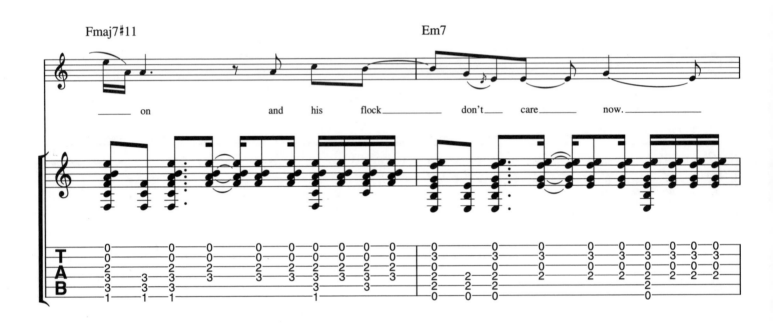

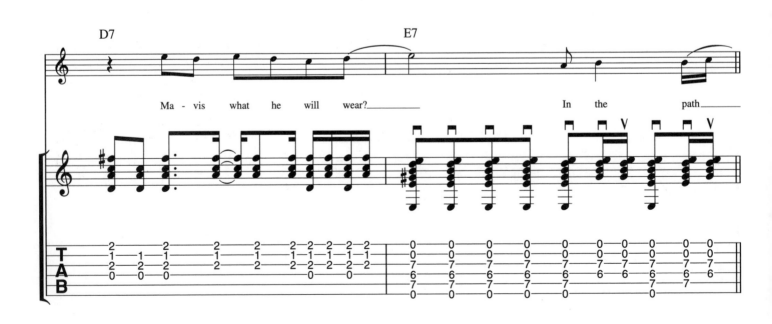

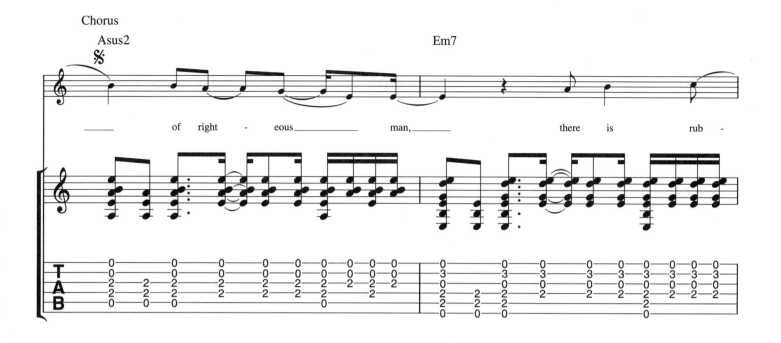

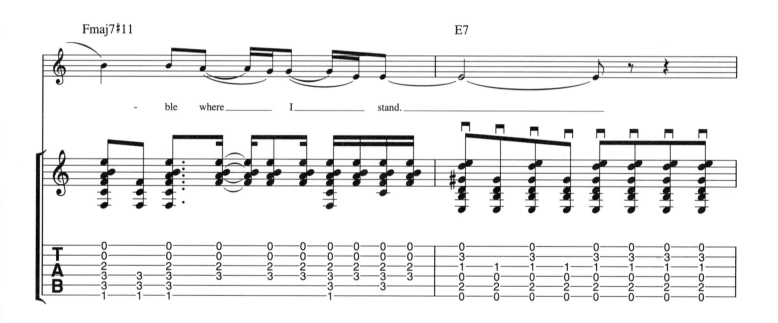

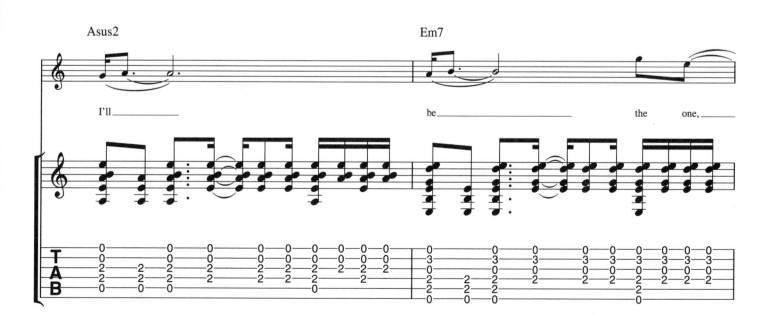

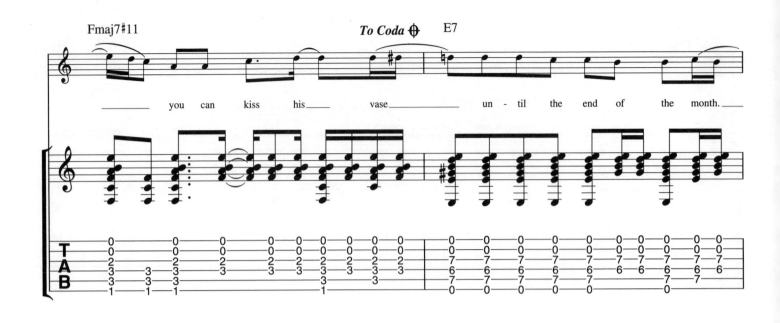

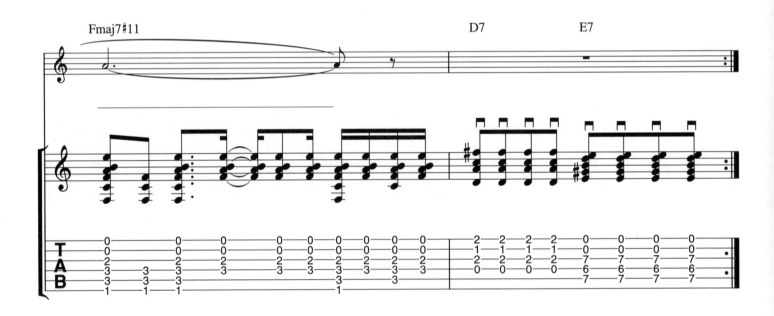

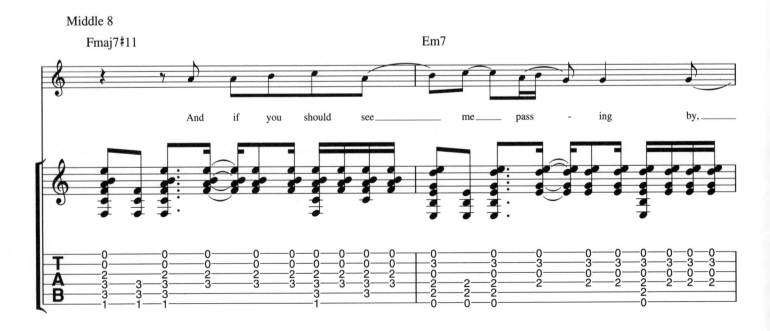

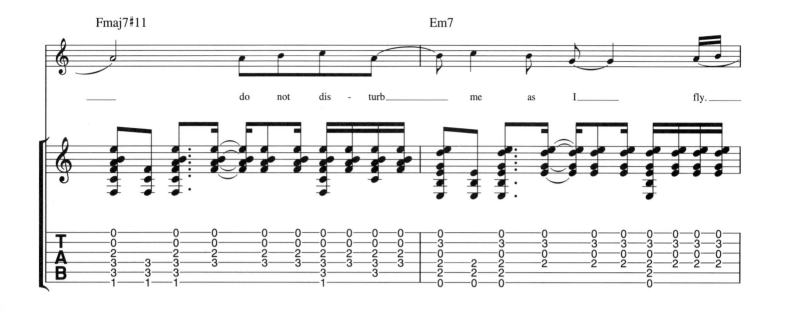

do not dis - turb____ me as I____ fly.

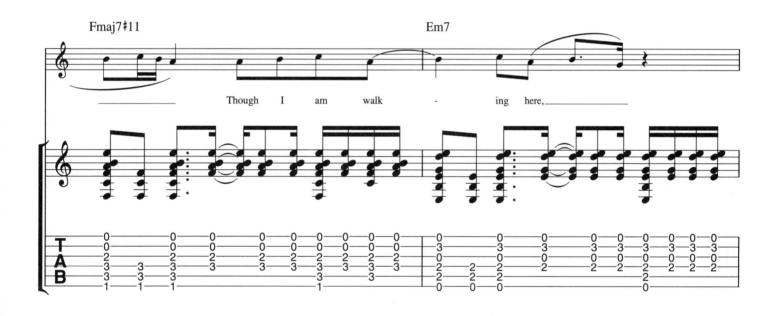

Though I am walk - ing here,____

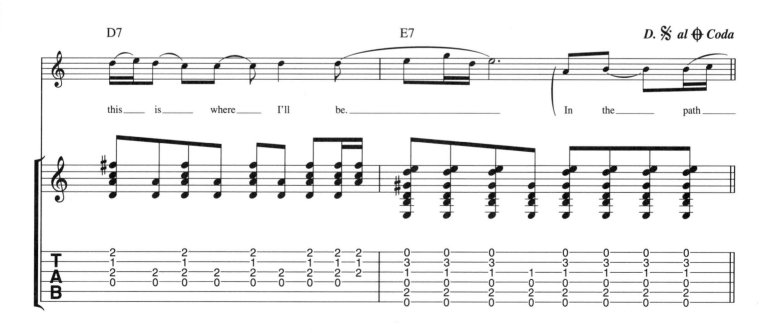

this__ is__ where__ I'll be.____ In the__ path__

D. %. al ⊕ Coda

Coda ⊕

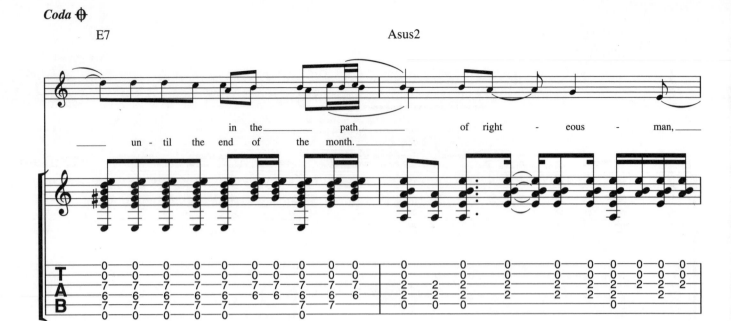

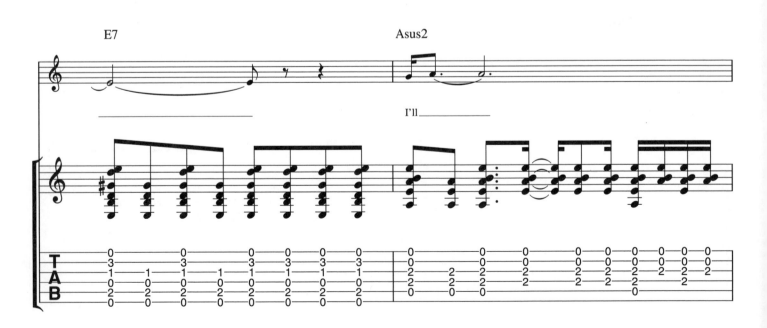

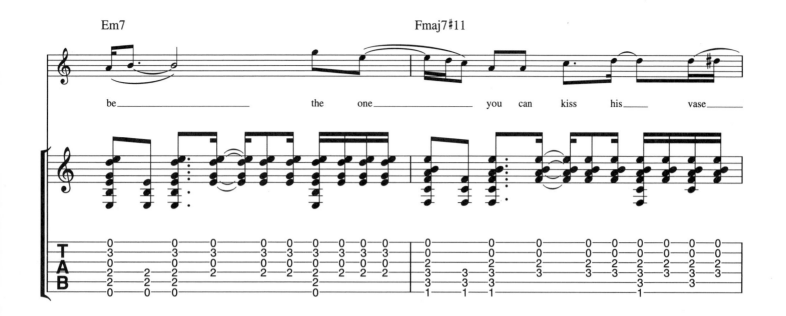

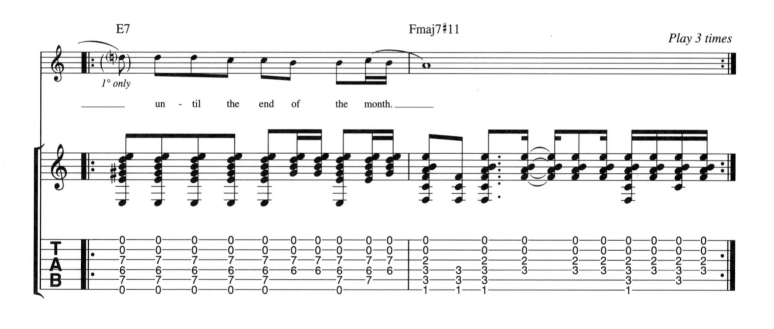

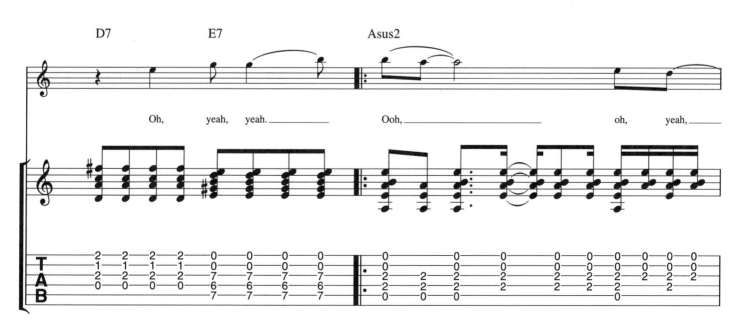

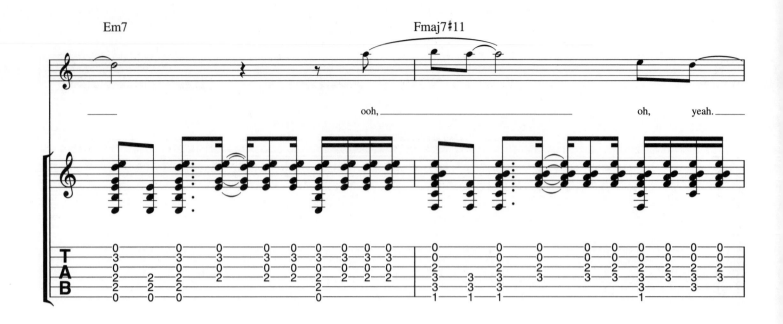

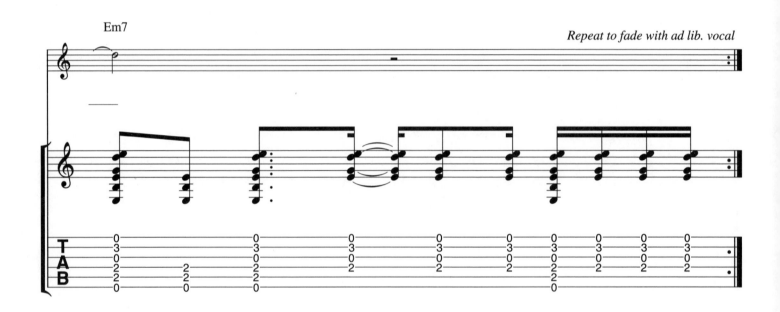

AN OPEN LETTER
MAYBE (TO THE LYRICAL TRAINSPOTTER)

WORDS & MUSIC BY PAUL DRAPER

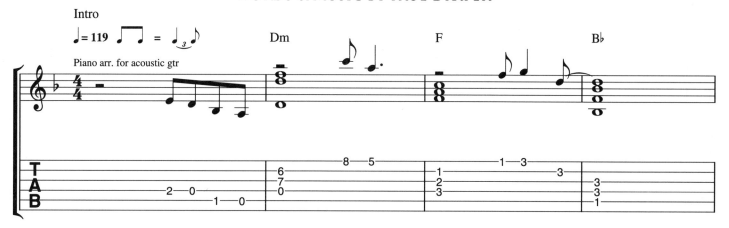

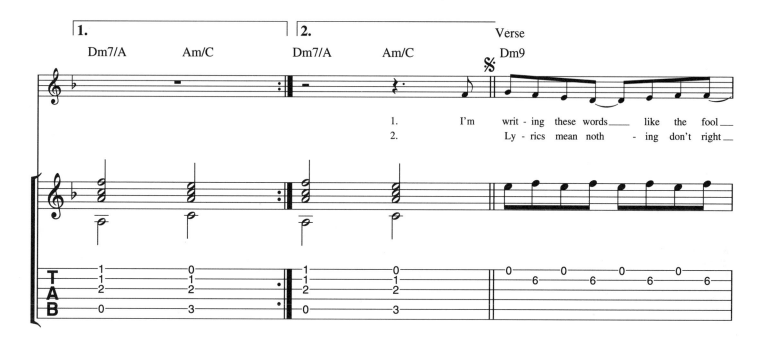

1. I'm writ-ing these words___ like the fool___
2. Ly - rics mean noth - ing don't right___

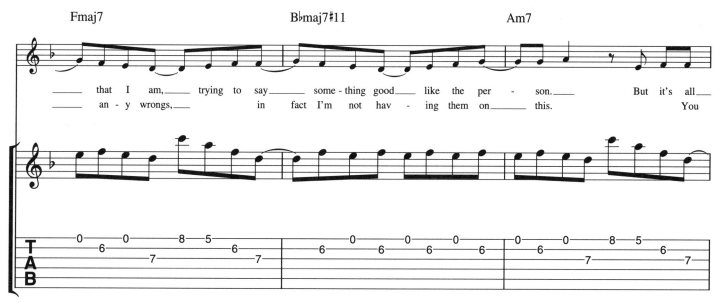

___ that I am,___ trying to say___ some-thing good___ like the per - son.___ But it's all___ You

___ an - y wrongs,___ in fact I'm not hav - ing them on___ this.

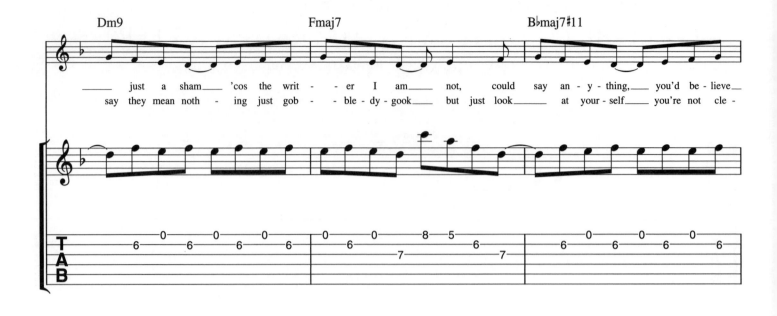

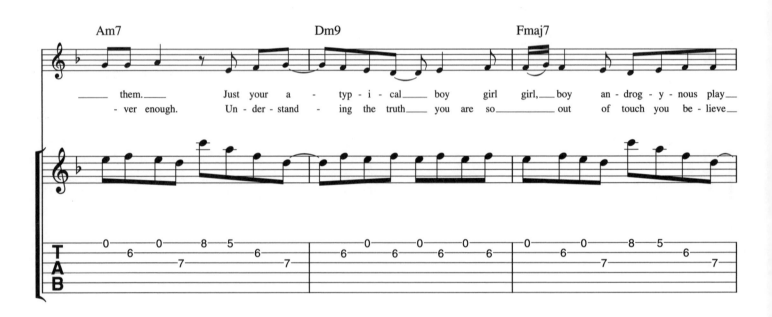

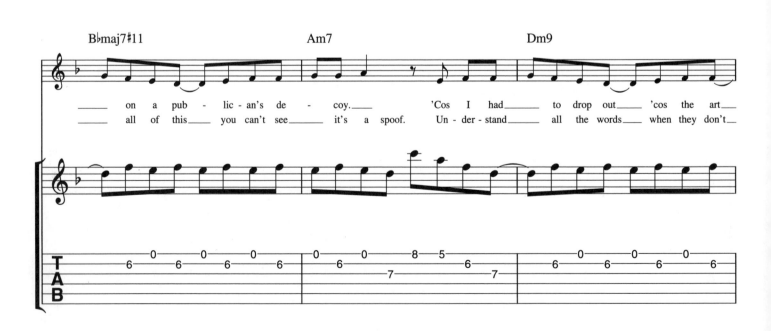

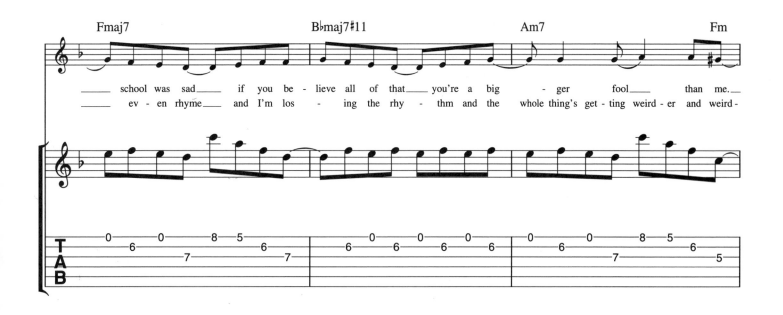

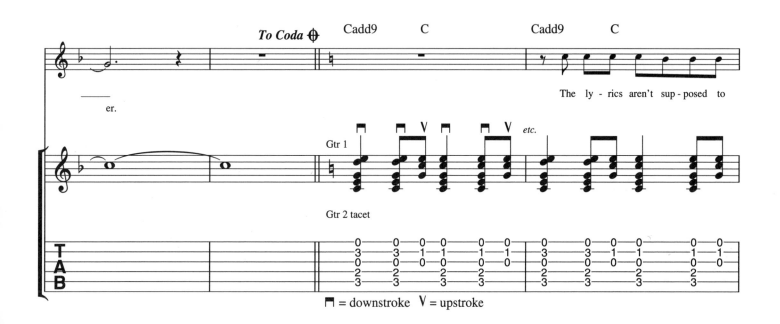

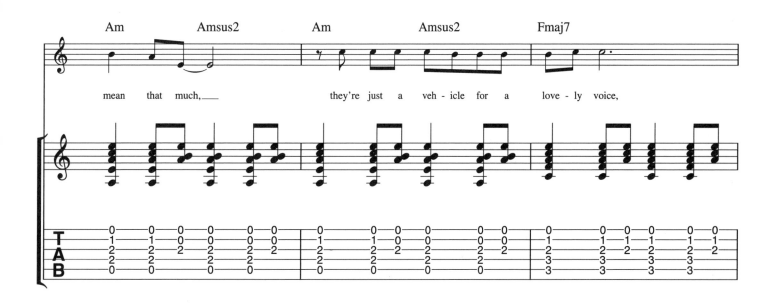

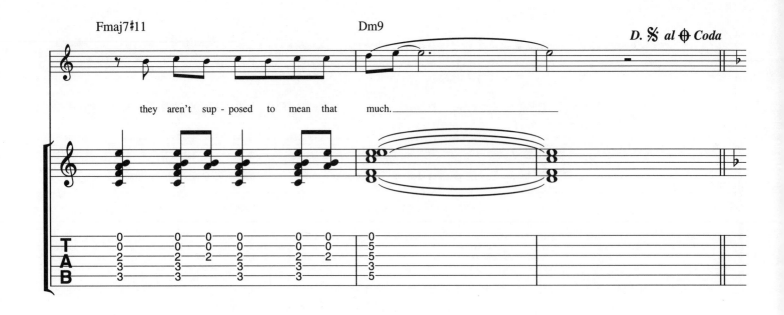

they aren't sup-posed to mean that much.____

D. %S al Coda

Coda

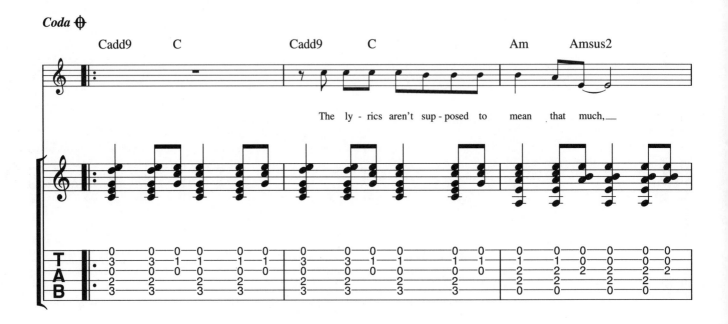

The ly-rics aren't sup-posed to mean that much,__

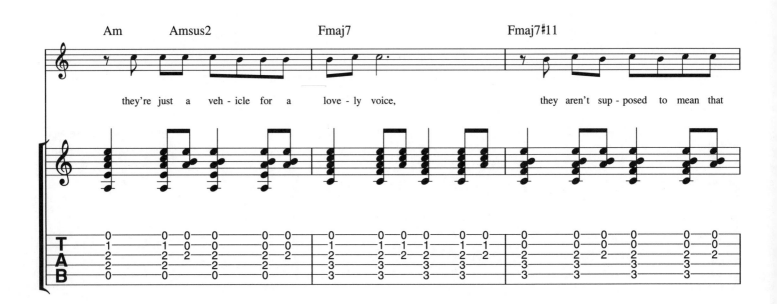

they're just a veh-icle for a love-ly voice, they aren't sup-posed to mean that

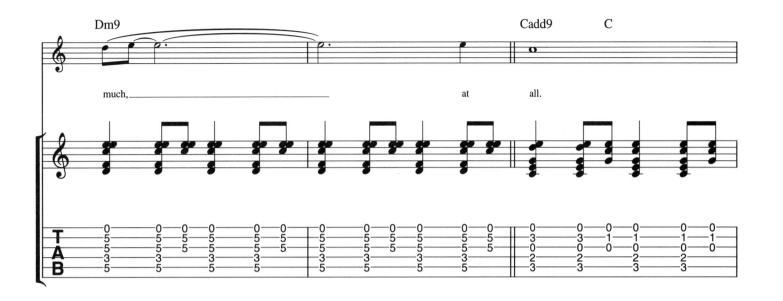

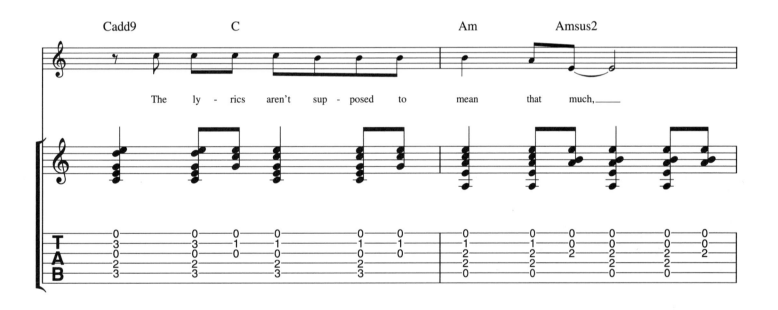

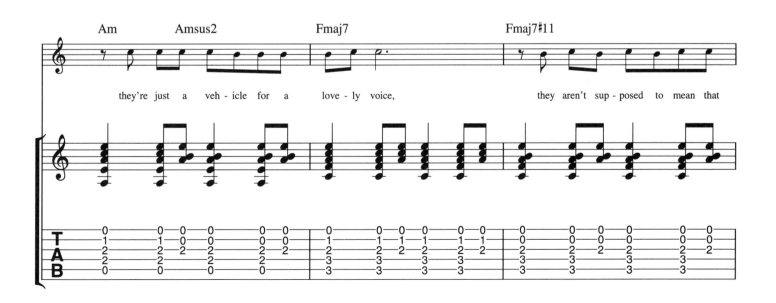

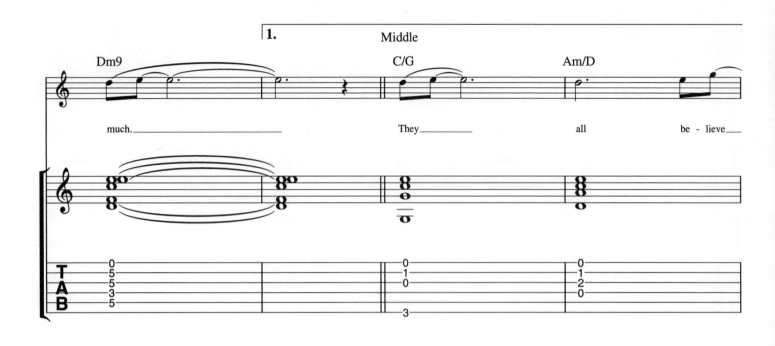

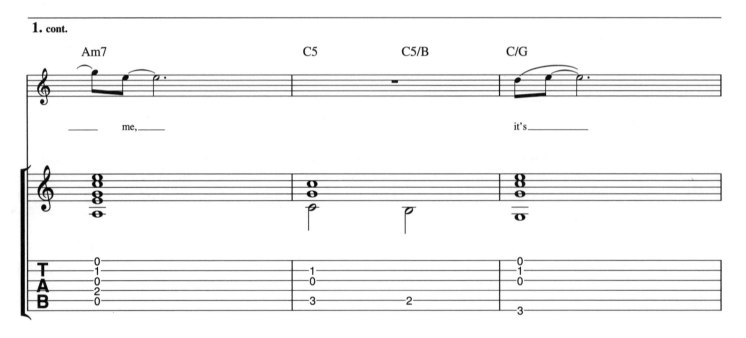

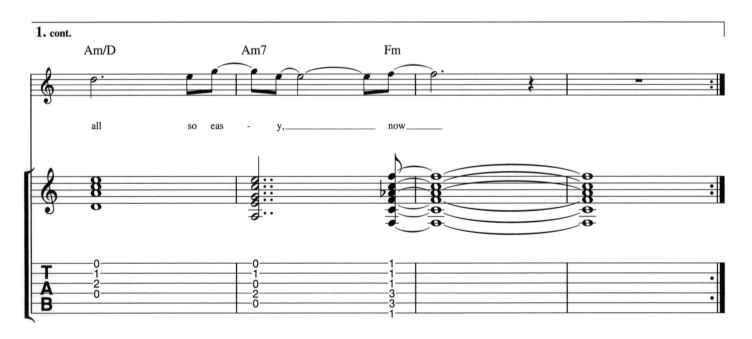

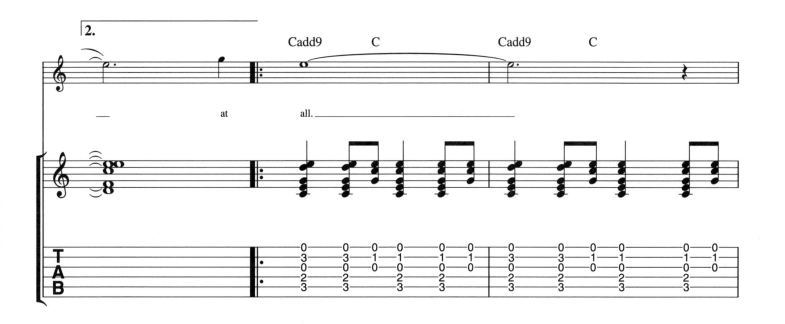

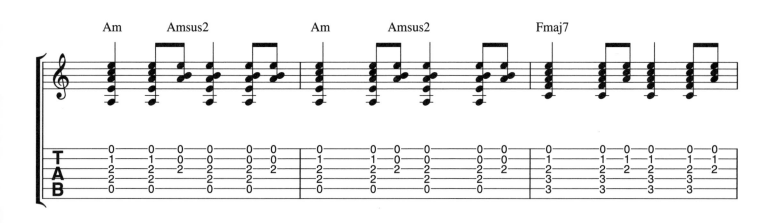

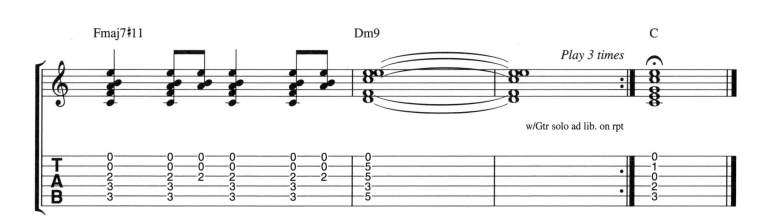